Scholastic Success With

KINDERGARTEN
WORKBOOK

■SCHOLASTIC

NEW YORK • TORONTO • LONDON
AUCKLAND • SYDNEY • NEW DELHI • HONG KONG

Cover design by Anna Christian; Cover art by Rob McClurkan
Interior illustrations by Janet Armbrust, Rusty Fletcher, Kathy Marlin, Julissa Mora, Sherry Neidigh, Danny E. Rivera, and Carol Tiernon
Interior design by Quack & Company

ISBN 978-1-338-30657-6

Scholastic Inc., 557 Broadway, New York, NY 10012
Copyright © 2018 Scholastic Inc.
All rights reserved. Printed in the U.S.A.

3 4 5 6 7 8 9 10   56   24 23 22 21 20

Table of Contents

THE ALPHABET

NUMBERS AND COUNTING

HANDWRITING

BASIC CONCEPTS

© Scholastic Inc.

SCIENCE

ITTY-BITTY WORD BOOKS

"Nothing succeeds like success."

Alexandre Dumas the Elder, 1854

Dear Parent,

Congratulations on choosing this excellent educational resource for your child. Scholastic has long been a leader in educational publishing—creating quality educational materials for use in school and at home for more than a century.

As a partner in your child's academic success, you'll want to get the most out of the learning experience offered in this book. To help your child learn at home, try following these helpful hints:

★ Provide a comfortable place to work.

★ Have frequent work sessions, but keep them short.

★ Praise your child's successes and encourage his or her efforts. Offer positive help when your child makes a mistake.

★ Display your child's work and share his or her progress with family and friends.

In this workbook you'll find hundreds of practice pages that keep kids challenged and excited as they strengthen their skills across the classroom curriculum.

The workbook is divided into seven sections: The Alphabet; Numbers and Counting; Handwriting; Basic Concepts; Phonics; Science; and Itty-Bitty Word Books. You and your child should feel free to move through the pages in any way you wish. The table of contents lists the activities and the skills practiced.

Take the lead and help your child succeed with the *Scholastic Success With Kindergarten* workbook!

FOCUS SKILLS

The activities in this workbook reinforce age-appropriate skills and will help your child meet the following standards established as goals by leading educators.

Mathematics

★ Understands that numerals are symbols used to represent quantities or attributes of real-world objects

★ Counts whole numbers

★ Understands symbolic, concrete, and pictorial representations of numbers

★ Understands basic whole number relationships

★ Understands basic properties of and similarities and differences between simple geometric shapes

★ Understands the common language of spatial sense

★ Understands that geometric shapes are useful for representing and describing real-world situations

★ Extends simple patterns

Writing

★ Uses conventions of print in writing (e.g., forms letters in print, uses upper- and lowercase letters of the alphabet, writes from left-to-right and top-to-bottom)

Reading

★ Understands that print conveys meaning

★ Uses basic elements of phonetic analysis (e.g., common letter/sound relationships, beginning and ending consonants, vowel sounds, blends, word patterns) to decode unknown words

★ Uses a picture dictionary to determine word meaning

★ Understands level-appropriate sight words and vocabulary

★ Uses reading skills and strategies to understand a variety of informational texts

Science

★ Understands plants and animals and their environments

★ Recognizes weather and seasonal patterns

★ Analyzes force and motion

THE ALPHABET

A Work of Art

Color each space with the letter **A** red.

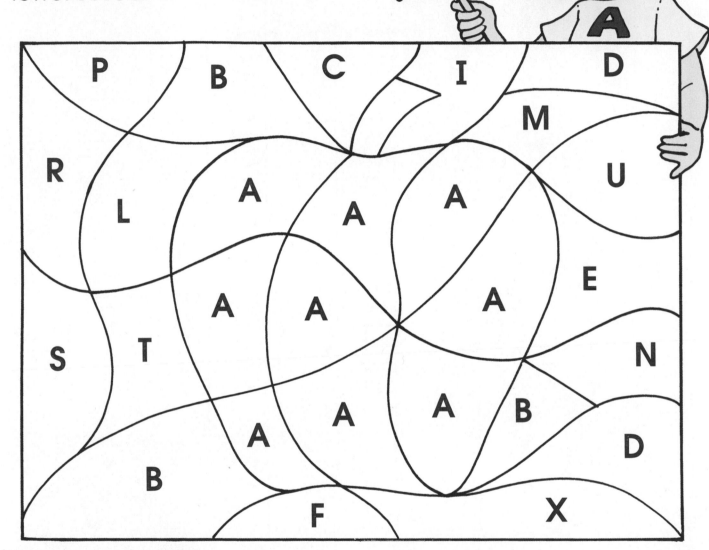

Trace and write.

A C

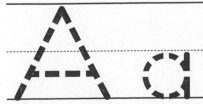 **Find an A in the newspaper.**

Name _____

❧ Trace the A and a's.

A̅l̅l̅i̅g̅a̅t̅o̅r̅ ̅p̅a̅i̅n̅t̅s̅ ̅a̅n̅ ̅a̅p̅p̅l̅e̅.

❧ Now write the A and a's.

l̲l̲i̲g̲a̲t̲o̲r̲ ̲p̲a̲i̲n̲t̲s̲ ̲____n̲ ̲____p̲p̲l̲e̲.

❧ Add a's and then read the words.

____pple

____lligator

____rm

Now draw and write your own **Aa** word.

The King's Castle

Follow the letter **C**. Color the path that leads to the castle.

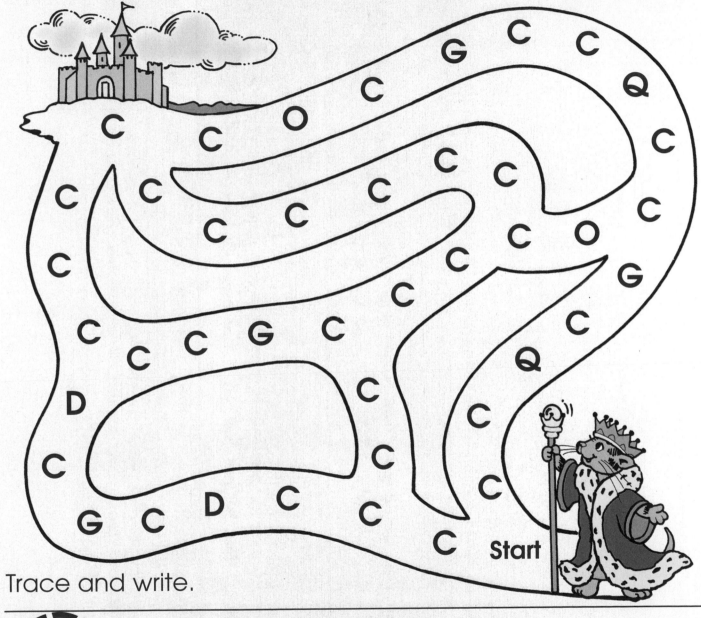

Trace and write.

 Cat begins with the letter C. On another sheet of paper, draw a cat.

Name _____

❧ Trace the C and c's.

Cleo carries cocoa.

❧ Now write the C and c's.

_leo _arries _ocoa.

❧ Add c's and then read the words.

___at	___ar	___ow	

Now draw and write
your own **Cc** word.

_____

Dandy Duck

Color each duck track with the letter **D** orange.

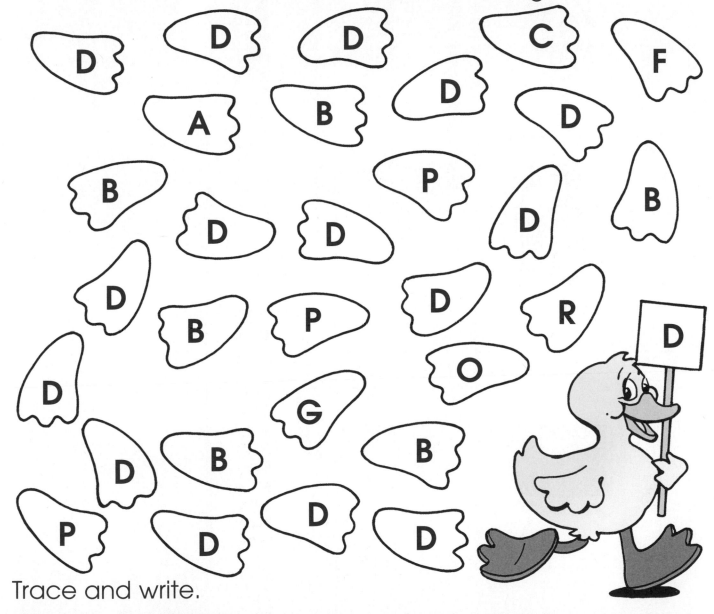

Trace and write.

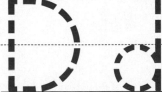

 On another sheet of paper, draw three different ducks.

Name _____

❧ Trace the D's and d.

Detective Dog likes doughnuts.

❧ Now write the D's and d.

etective ___og likes ___oughnuts.

etective ___og likes ___oughnuts.

❧ Add d's and then read the words.

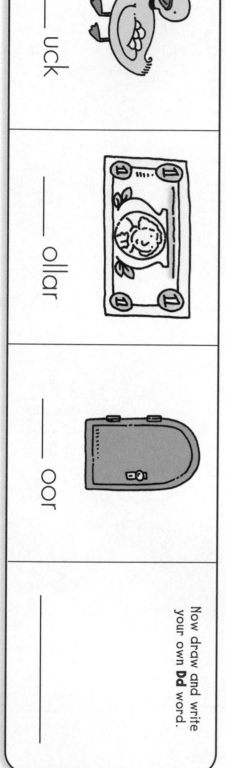

___uck	___ollar	___oor

Now draw and write your own **Dd** word.

_____

Eggs Everywhere!

Find and color each egg with the letter **E**.

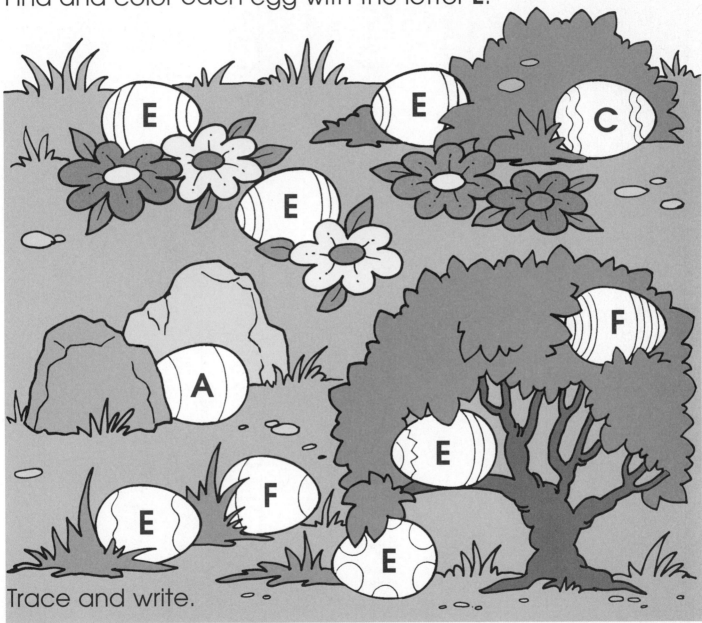

Trace and write.

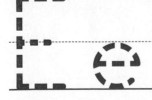

 On another sheet of paper, draw and color two decorated eggs.

Name _____

❧ Trace the E's.

E|vin the E|ephant makes an (E).

❧ Now write the E's and e.

____|vin the ____|ephant makes an ____.

❧ Add e's and then read the words.

_____ lbow

_____ ye

_____ gg

Now draw and write
your own **Ee** word.

_____

In Full Bloom

Color each space with the letter **F** yellow.
Color all the other spaces blue.

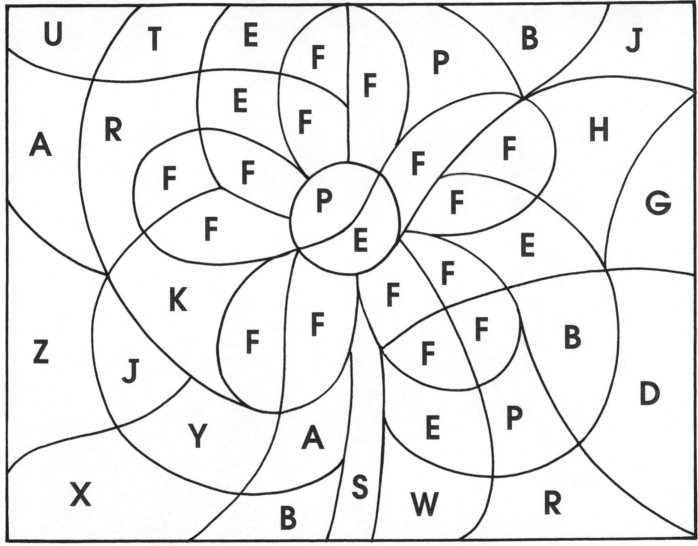

Trace and write.

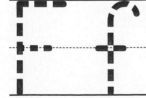

 Flower begins with the letter F. On another sheet of paper, draw a red flower.

Name _____

☘ Trace the F's and f.

F ̣f̣i the Ferret plays the flute.

☘ Now write the F's and f.

____f̣i the ____erret plays the ____lute.

☘ Add f's and then read the words.

___eather	___ish	___ork

Now draw and write your own **Ff** word.

_____

A Grape-Eating Gorilla

Follow the letter **G**. Color the path that leads to the grapes.

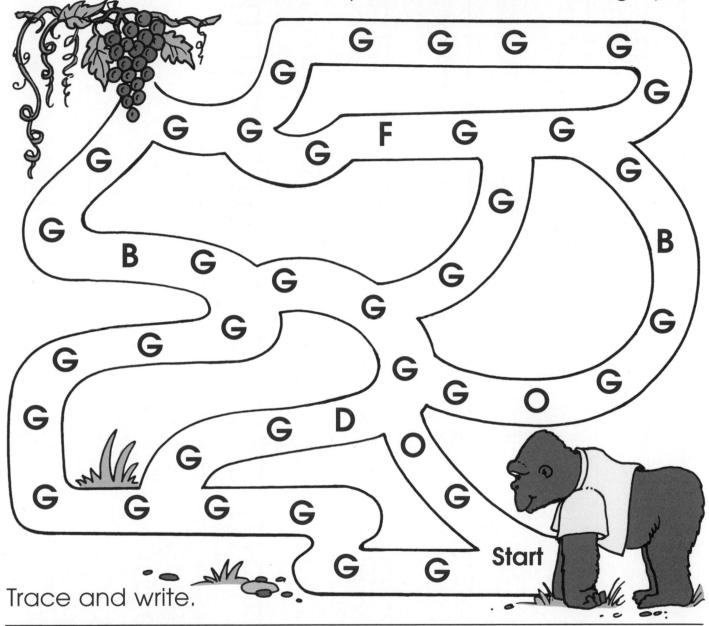

Trace and write.

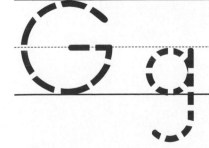

© Scholastic Inc.

Name _____

✎ Trace the G and g's.

$\overset{2}{\underset{1}{G}}$orilla $\overset{1}{\underset{2}{g}}$obbles $\overset{1}{\underset{2}{g}}$ooseberries.

✎ Now write the G and g's.

____orilla ____obbles ____ooseberries.

✎ Add g's and then read the words.

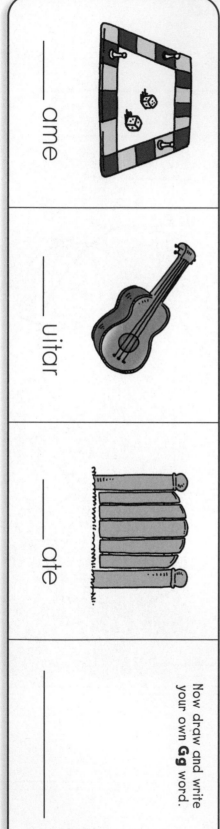

____ame

____uitar

____ate

Now draw and write your own **Gg** word.

_____

Hippo's Hats

Color each hat with the letter **H**.

Trace and write.

 On another sheet of paper, draw a picture of a word that rhymes with hat.

© Scholastic Inc.

Name _____

❖ Trace the H and h.

Hippo is hiding.

❖ Now write the H and h.

_____ippo is hiding.

_____ippo is _____iding.

❖ Add h's and then read the words.

____air	____at	____ouse

Now draw and write your own **Hh** word.

_____

Icky Insects

Color each insect with the letter **I**.

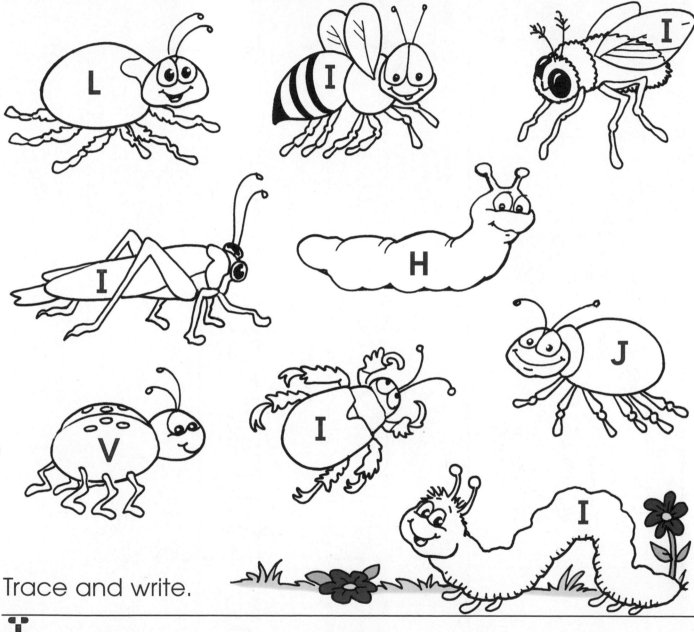

Trace and write.

 On another sheet of paper, draw a picture of something you think is icky.

Name _____

✿ Trace the I and i's.

Iguana is on an iceberg.

✿ Now write the I and i's.

_____ guana _s on an _ceberg.

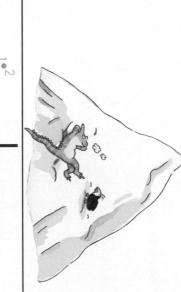

✿ Add i's and then read the words.

Now draw and write your own **Ii** word.

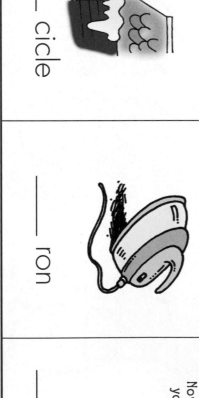

___ ce cream	___ cicle	___ ron

Jelly Beans

Color each jelly bean with the letter **J**.

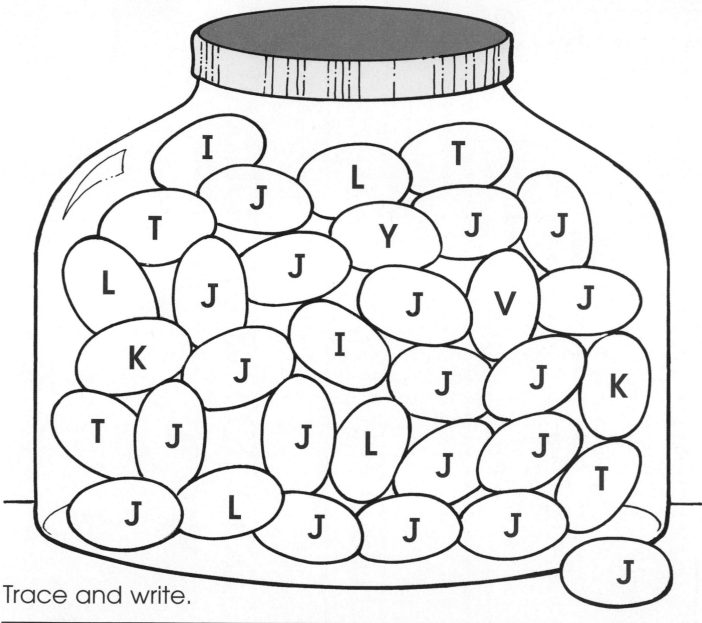

Trace and write.

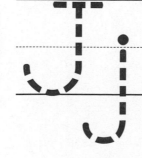

Name _____

✿ Trace the J and j.

J̲aguar loves J̲am.

✿ Now write the J and j.

_____aguar loves _____am.

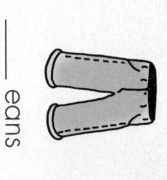

✿ Add j's and then read the words.

_____ar	_____ump	_____eans

Now draw and write your own **Jj** word.

_____

© Scholastic Inc.

Colorful Kites

Draw a line from each kite with the letter **K** to the boy.
Color each kite with the letter **K**.

Trace and write.

 On another sheet of paper, draw a picture of a beautiful kite.

Name

❧ Trace the K and k.

Kangaroo plays Kazoo.

❧ Now write the K and k.

_____ angaroo plays _____ azoo.

❧ Add k's and then read the words.

_____ ing

_____ ite

_____ angaroo

Now draw and write
your own **Kk** word.

_____

Check It Out!

Find and circle each letter **L** hidden in the library.

Reading Is Fun!

Trace and write.

Check out a book from the library.

Name _____

❧ Trace the L and l's.

L̲amb l̲oves to l̲augh.

❧ Now write the L and l's.

____amb ____oves to ____augh.

____amb ____oves to ____augh.

❧ Add l's and then read the words.

____emon   ____eaf   ____ion

Now draw and write
your own **Ll** word.

_____

Musical Mouse

Follow the letter **M**. Color the path that leads the mouse to the mandolin.

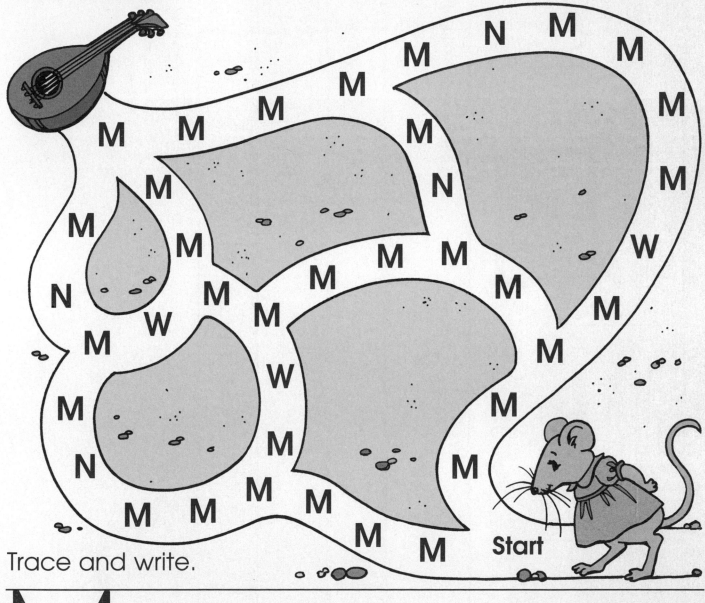

Trace and write.

 On another sheet of paper, draw a picture of a mouse house.

Name _____

❧ Trace the M and m's.

Monkey mops milk.

❧ Now write the M and m's.

____onkey ____ops ____ilk.

Now draw and write your own **Mm** word.

❧ Add m's and then read the words.

____ouse	____ap	____onkey

Noodle Doodle Soup

Circle each **N** in the bowl of soup.

G N H N K
N Z F E N
A D B L N J
A N I C N

Trace and write.

N n

© Scholastic Inc.

Name _____

❧ Trace the N's and n.

$\overset{1}{\underset{3}{\overset{2}{N}}}$ate the $\overset{1}{\underset{3}{\overset{2}{N}}}$ewt has a $\overset{1}{\overset{2}{n}}$ickel.

❧ Now write the N's and n.

_____ate the _____ewt has a _____ickel.

❧ Add n's and then read the words.

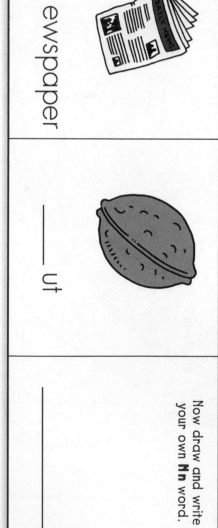

_____est   _____ewspaper   _____ut

Now draw and write
your own **Nn** word.

_____

What Is Ollie?

Color each space with the letter **O** purple. Color all the other spaces blue.

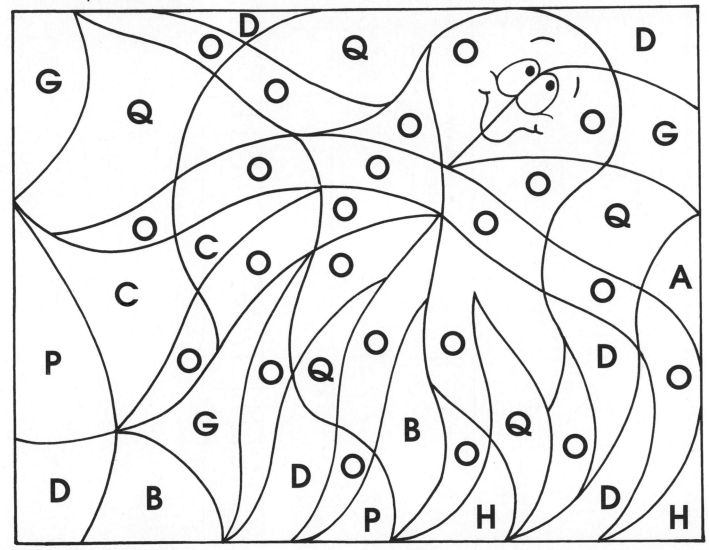

Trace and write.

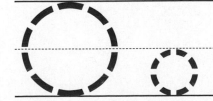

 Orange begins with the letter O. On another sheet of paper, draw an orange.

Name _____

❖ Trace the O and o's.

Olive the octopus loves onions.

❖ Now write the O and o's.

___ive the ___ctopus loves ___nions.

❖ Add o's and then read the words.

___wl   ___ctopus   ___ven

Now draw and write
your own **Oo** word.

Plenty of Popcorn

Help Pete find his popcorn. Color each piece of popcorn with the letter **P**.

Trace and write.

Name _____

❧ Trace the p's.

The pigs planned a picnic.

❧ Now write the p's.

The __igs __lanned a __icnic.

❧ Add p's and then read the words.

___ail	___encil	___an

Now draw and write your own **P p** word.

The Queen's Quilt

Color each space with the letter **Q** yellow.
Color all the other spaces green.

Trace and write.

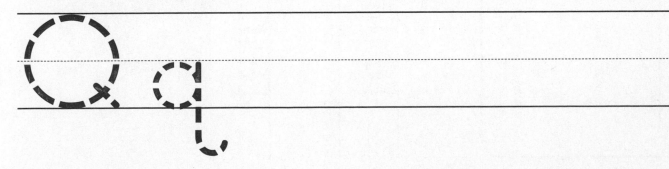

Name _____

❧ Trace the Q's and q.

Quincy Quail likes quiet.

❧ Now write the Q's and q.

_____uincy _____uail likes _____uiet.

❧ Add q's and then read the words.

____ueen	____uilt	____uiet	

Now draw and write your own **Qq** word.

_____

Raindrops

Find and circle each letter **R** on the umbrella. Color each raindrop with the letter **R** blue.

Trace and write.

 Rainbow begins with the letter R. On another sheet of paper, draw a rainbow.

Name _____

❖ Trace the R's and r's.

Rosie Rabbit rakes rocks.

❖ Now write the R's and r's.

___osie ___abbit ___akes ___ocks.

❖ Add r's and then read the words.

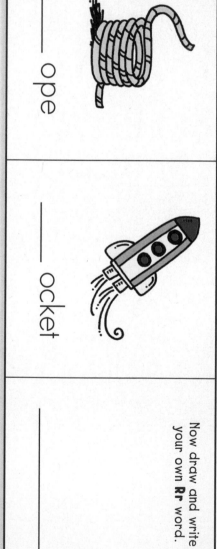

| ___abbit | ___ope | ___ocket |

Now draw and write your own **Rr** word.

Building a Sand Castle

Find and circle each letter **S**.

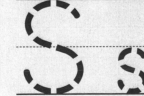

Trace and write.

Sandwich begins with the letter S. On another sheet of paper, draw a picture of your favorite sandwich.

Name _____

❦ Trace the S and s.

Seal makes a Sandwich.

❦ Now write the S and s.

___eal makes a ___andwich.

❦ Add s's and then read the words.

_____ andwich

_____ ock

_____ oap

Now draw and write
your own **Ss** word.

_____

© Scholastic Inc.

Fast Track

Follow the letter **T**. Color the path that leads Tommy Train to the station.

Trace and write.

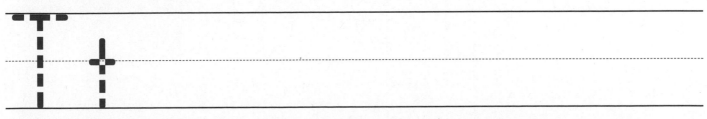

Turtle begins with the letter T. On another sheet of paper, draw a picture of a turtle.

Name _____

Trace the T's and t's.

Tilly Turtle takes a taxi.

Now write the T's and t's.

_illy _urtle _akes a _axi.

Add t's and then read the words.

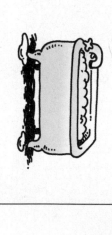

___ent

___oothbrush

___ub

Now draw and write
your own **Tt** word.

_____

Under the Umbrella

Circle each letter **U**.

Trace and write.

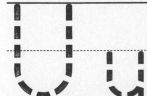

 Under begins with the letter U. On another sheet of paper, draw a picture of something hiding under a shell.

Name _____

❧ Trace the U and u.

U mbrellabird rides a Unicycle.

❧ Now write the U and u.

___ mbrellabird rides a ___ nicycle.

Now draw and write
your own **Uu** word.

❧ Add u's and then read the words.

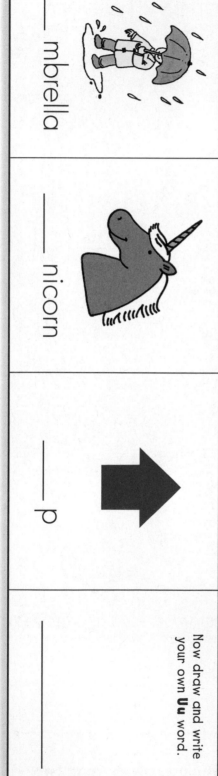

___ mbrella ___ nicorn ➡ ___ p ___

© Scholastic Inc.

Voting for Veggies

Color each veggie green that has the letter **V** hidden on it.

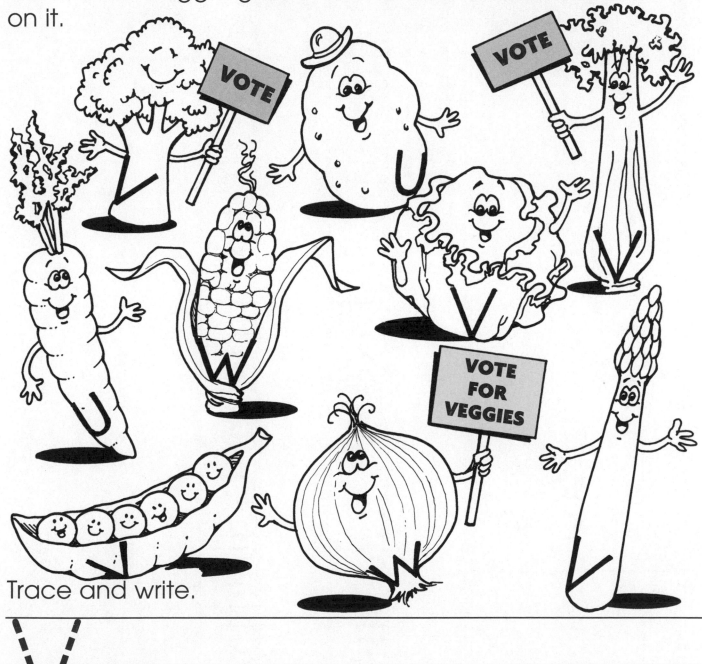

Trace and write.

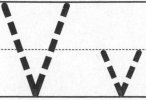

 Veggie begins with the letter V. On another sheet of paper, draw your two favorite veggies.

Name _____

❧ Trace the V's and v.

Vera Viper has a Valentine.

❧ Now write the V's and v.

__era __iper has a __alentine.

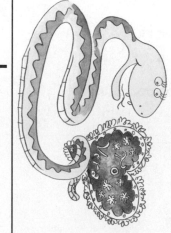

❧ Add v's and then read the words.

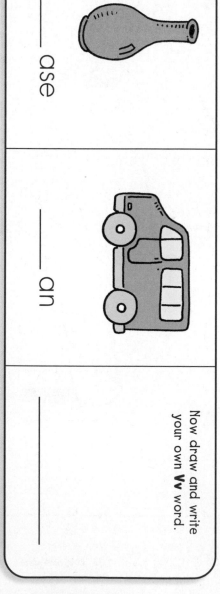

___est   ___ase   ___an

Now draw and write
your own **Vv** word.

_____

Guess Who?

Color each space with the letter **W** green. Color all the other spaces brown.

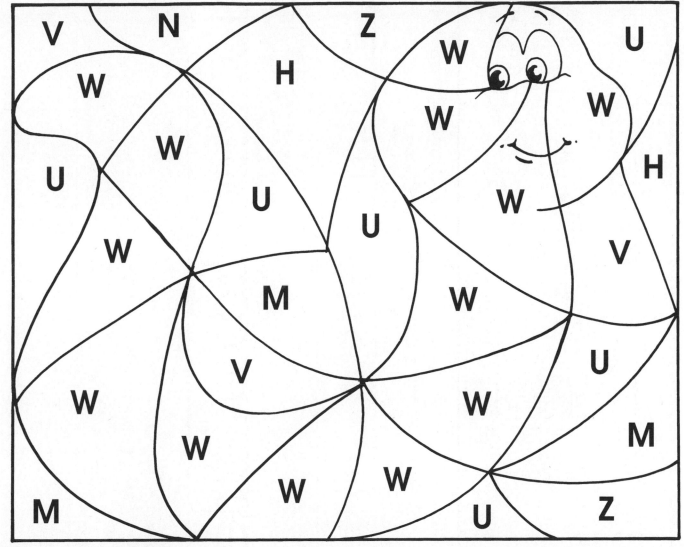

Trace and write.

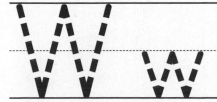

 Whale begins with the letter W. On another sheet of paper, draw a big whale.

Name _____

❊ Trace the W and w.

Worm had a Wagon.

❊ Now write the W and w.

___orm had a ___agon.

❊ Add w's and then read the words.

Now draw and write
your own **Ww** word.

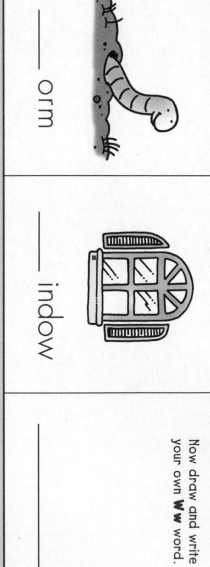

___eb	___orm	___indow	

X Marks the Spot!

Follow the letter **X**. Help the girl find her way to the treasure chest.

Start

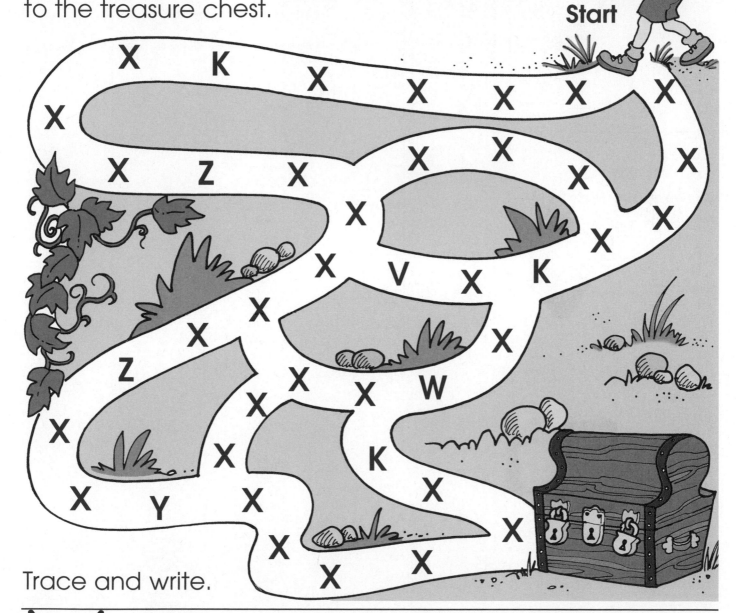

Trace and write.

  Draw five X's in a row.

Name _____

🖐 Trace the X and x.

X̶-̶R̶a̶y̶ ̶f̶i̶s̶h̶ ̶p̶l̶a̶y̶s̶ ̶x̶y̶l̶o̶p̶h̶o̶n̶e̶.

🖐 Now write the X and x.

___-Ray fish plays ___ylophone.

🖐 Add x's and then read the words.

fo___

___ylophone

___-ray

Now draw and write
your own **Xx** word.

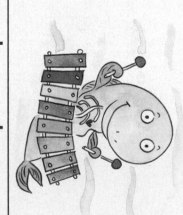

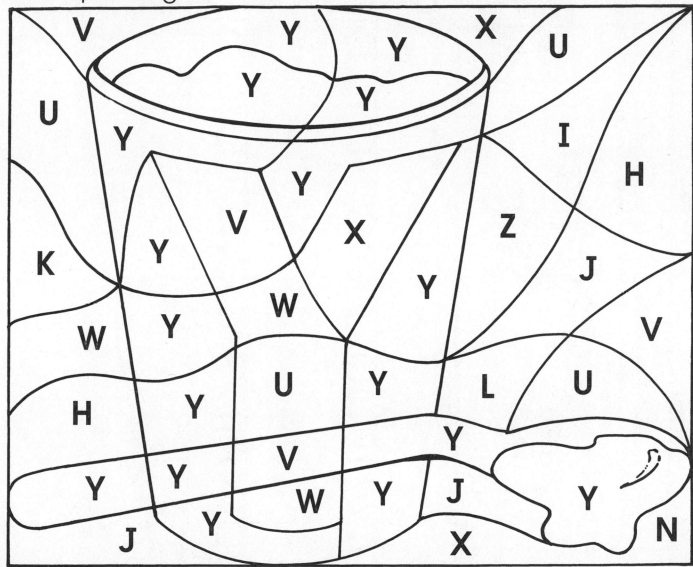

Yummy Yogurt

Color each space with the letter **Y** yellow. Color all the other spaces green.

Trace and write.

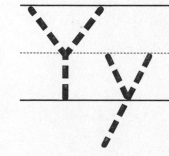

Name _____

🍀 Trace the y's.

The yak ate yogurt.

🍀 Now write the y's.

The ___ak ate ___ogurt.

🍀 Add y's and then read the words.

___arn	___ard	___o-yo	

Now draw and write your own **Yy** word.

Zany Zookeeper

The zookeeper lost the zebra. Find and circle each letter **Z**.

Trace and write.

💡 **Zero begins with the letter Z. Draw five zeros in a row.**

Name _____

❧ Trace the Z and z.

The Zebra lives at the Zoo.

❧ Now write the Z and z.

The ___ebra lives at the ___oo.

Now draw and write
your own **Zz** word.

❧ Add z's and then read the words.

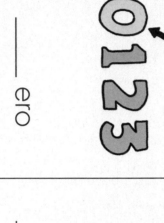	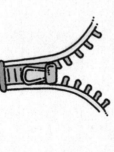	
___ebra	___ero	___ipper

Band of Ants

Color each drum with the letter **a** red.
Color each drum with the letter **b** blue.
Color each drum with the letter **c** green.

Trace and write.

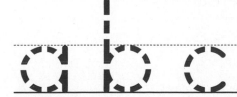

 On a sheet of lined paper, write Aa, Bb, Cc.

Dinosaur Dig

Follow the letters **d**, **e**, **f** in order. Color the path that leads to the dinosaur bones.

Trace and write.

Look in the newspaper to find the letters d, e, and f.

Inch by Inch

To find out what insect moves about an inch at a time, color each space with the letter **g** orange. Color each space with the letter **h** yellow. Color each space with the letter **i** black.

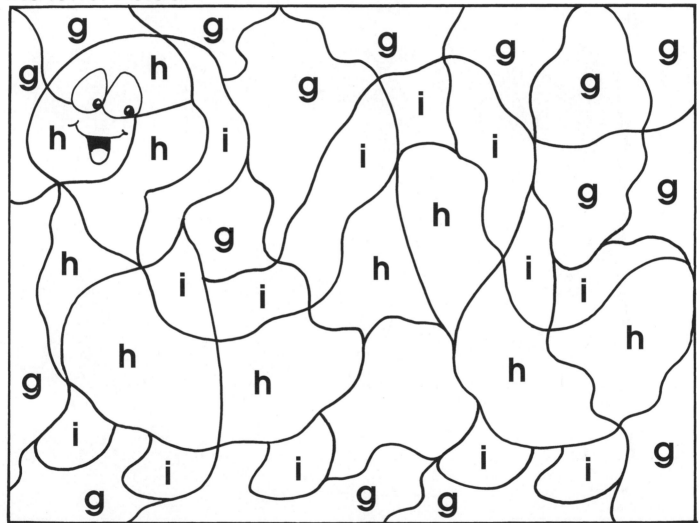

Trace and write.

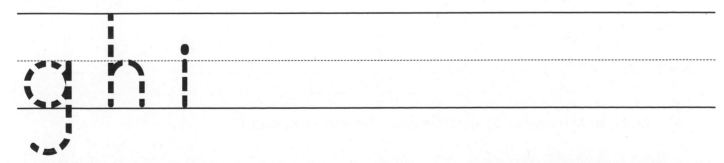

Kicking Kangaroos

Draw a line from each kangaroo to the soccer balls with the same letter.

Trace and write.

Ocean of Letters

Find and circle the letters **m**, **n**, and **o** in the picture.

Trace and write.

 On a sheet of lined paper, write the letters m, n, and o with their matching capital letters.

Plenty of Penguins

Circle each penguin with the letter **p**. Mark an *X* on each penguin with the letter **q**. Underline each penguin with the letter **r**.

Trace and write.

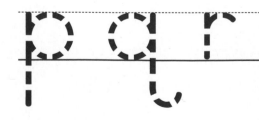

Spotted Turtle

Color each space with the letters **s**, **t**, or **u** to find a hidden letter.

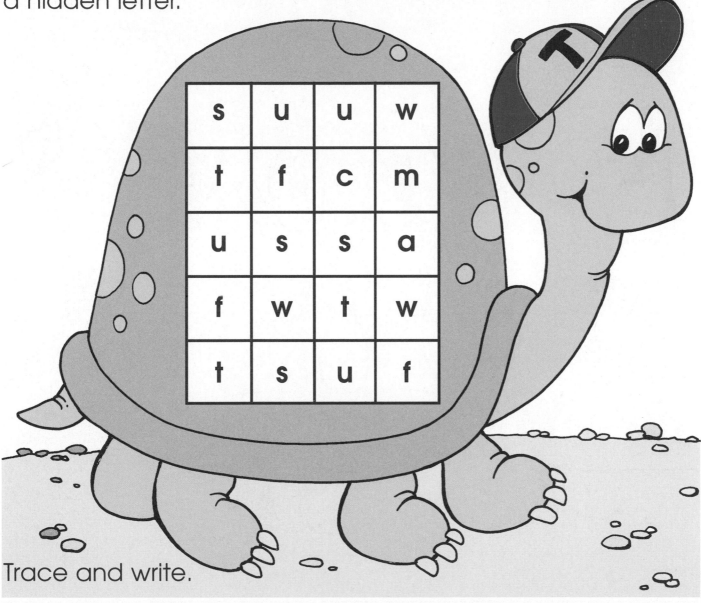

s	u	u	w
t	f	c	m
u	s	s	a
f	w	t	w
t	s	u	f

Trace and write.

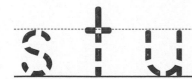

 Circle the hidden letter. s t u

Watermelon Fun

Color each seed with the letters **v**, **w**, or **x** black.

Trace and write.

 On another sheet of paper, draw a picture of your favorite fruit.

Follow the Yellow Brick Road

Follow the letters **y** and **z**. Color the road that leads to the zoo.

Start

Trace and write.

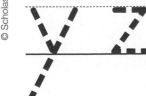

Careers From A to Z

Finish the alphabet.

A

G

M

VOTE
MAYOR

P

Z

 On another sheet of paper, draw a picture of what you would like to be when you grow up.

© Scholastic Inc.

Lost and Found

Find and circle each uppercase letter of the alphabet in the picture.

A B C D E F G H I J K L M
N O P Q R S T U V W X Y Z

 Circle the letter your first name begins with in the letter box above.

ABC Picture

Connect the dots in ABC order to find the hidden picture.
Tell a story about the picture.

Write It Right!

Write the missing lowercase letters.

	a		c
d			h
			m
n			
			w
	y		

Playing in the Park

Find and circle each lowercase letter of the alphabet in the picture. Say the letters as you find them.

a b c d e f g h i j k l m
n o p q r s t u v w x y z

Letters on Parade

Connect the dots from **a** to **z**.

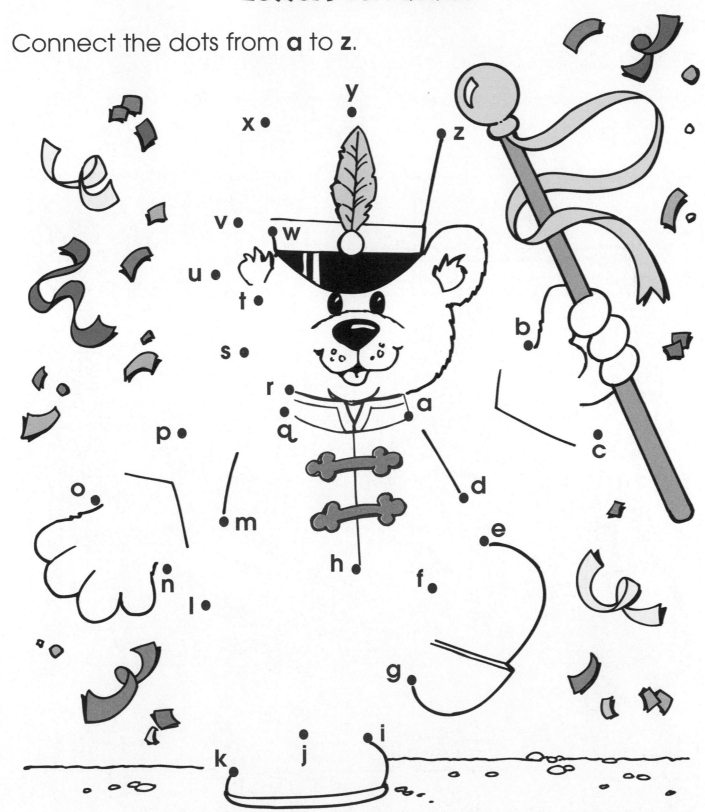

© Scholastic Inc.

Be a Better Builder

Write the lowercase letter.

A____

D____   G____   J____

L____   N____   P____

S____   U____   W____

Y____   K____   Q____

O____   B____   R____

 On a sheet of lined paper, write the first and last letters of your name.

© Scholastic Inc.

Match and Learn

Draw a line from each uppercase letter to the matching lowercase letter.

A   c   O   t

B   d   P   s

C   a   Q   q

D   b   R   o

E   g   S   p

F   f   T   r

G   e   U

H   k   V   z

I   l   W   x

J   h   X   v

K   m   Y   w

L   j   Z   y

M   n

N   i

Ask the people in your home what uppercase letters begin their names.

Clowning Around

Match the letter on each clown to its lowercase letter.

NUMBERS AND COUNTING

Zero at the Zoo

Trace and write.

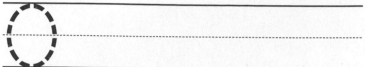

O _____

Zero is the number word for 0. Zero means none.
Circle the number that tells how many.

bears

0   1   2   3   4

birds

0   1   2   3   4

penguins

0   1   2   3   4

lions

0   1   2   3   4

camels

0   1   2   3   4

ducks

0   1   2   3   4

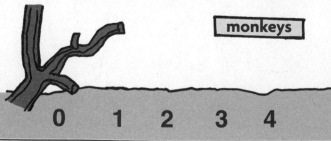

monkeys

0   1   2   3   4

seals

0   1   2   3   4

© Scholastic Inc.

One Old Octopus

Trace and write.

Color each shape with 1 fish.

An Underwater Home

Count each group of things found in the sea. Color one of each.

 How many objects did you color?

© Scholastic Inc.

Two Talking Turtles

Trace and write.

2

Color each circle with 2 dots.

Count how many telephones you have at home.

Mrs. Tacky Turtle

Circle the number that tells how many.

		1	2
		1	2
		1	2
		1	2
		1	2
		1	2
		1	2

 What else could Mrs. Turtle wear? Draw 2 of them.

Three Tiny Tugboats

Trace and write.

3

Color each barge with 3 objects.

Draw 3 logs on each barge.

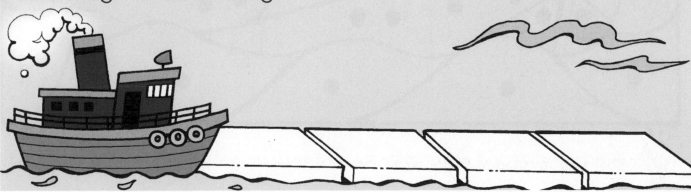

Tugboat Tow

Use the code to color the picture.

1 blue 2 brown 3 red

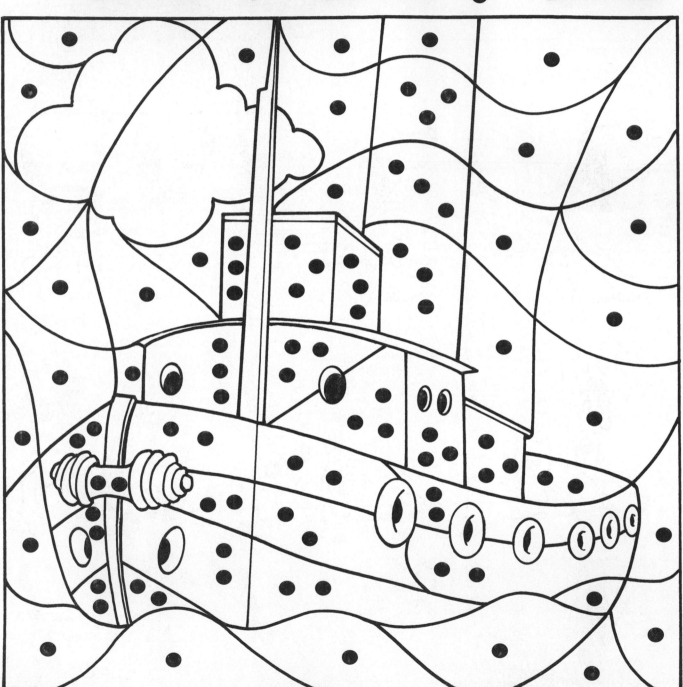

Which color did you use to color the most spaces?

Four Fine Firefighters

Trace and write.

Color each dog with 4 spots.

Climb to the Top

Count the objects on each step. Circle the matching number.

💡 **How many steps have 4 objects?** _____

Five Friendly Frogs

Trace and write.

5 _____

Color each lily pad with 5 flies.

Fast Frogs

Color each rock with 5 bugs to find which frog finishes first.

 How many rocks have 4 bugs? _____

Six Smelly Shoes

Trace and write.

Circle 6 shoes in each box.

Draw more shoes to make 6.

Count the socks. Circle the right number.   5   6   7

© Scholastic Inc.

Two Make a Pair

Count the shapes on each shoe. Draw a line to the matching number.

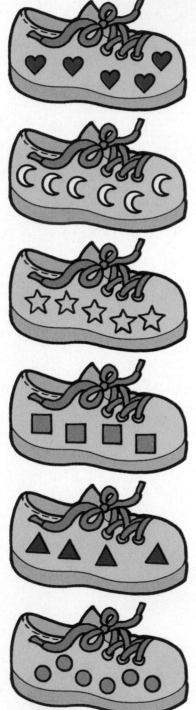

Count the shoes in your closet. How many shoes did you count?

Seven Seashells

Trace and write.

7 _____

Color 7 shells in each box.

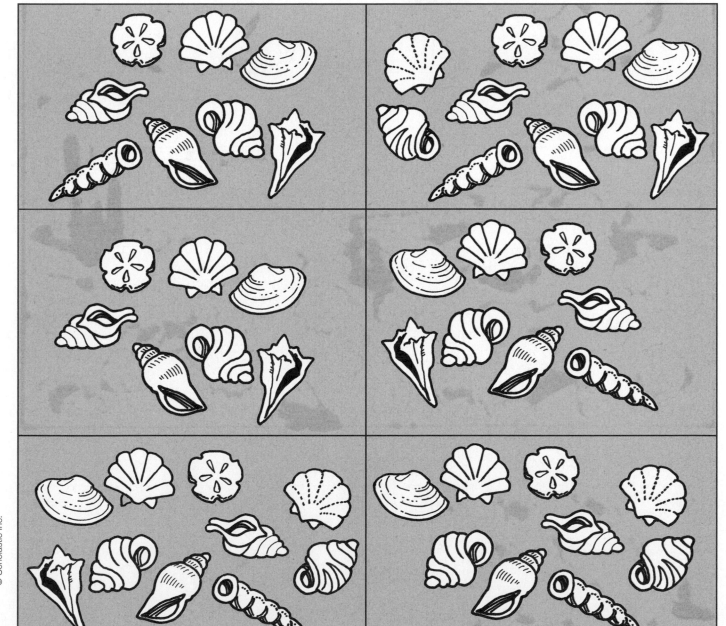

Seashells by the Seashore

Count each kind of shell in the picture. Write the total number next to the correct shell. Circle the shells that total 7.

How many? _____   How many? _____

How many? _____   How many? _____

Circle the number that tells how many.

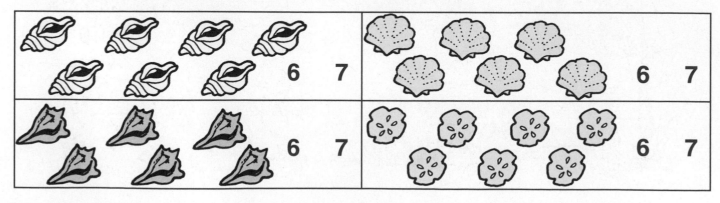

Eight Electric Eels

Trace and write.

Draw more eels to make 8.

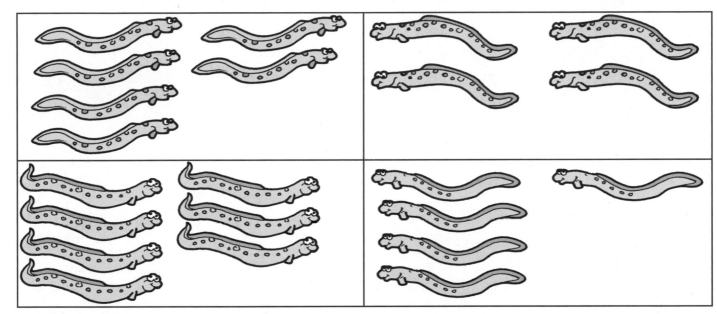

Count the eels. Color the matching number.

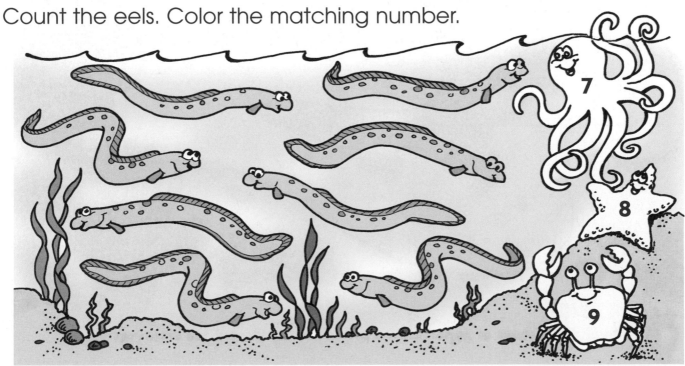

Eddie Eel Is Lost

Help Eddie Eel find his way back to the cave. Trace the path that goes in order from 1 to 8.

 On another sheet of paper, draw a picture of 8 different sea creatures.

Nine Nice Nectarines

Trace and write.

9

Color each basket that has 9 pieces of fruit.

Going to the Market

FRESH FRUIT

Count. Write how many. Color each fruit with 9.

On another sheet of paper, draw 9 pieces of your favorite fruit.

© Scholastic Inc.

Ten Railroad Ties

Trace and write.

I 0

Help Tina Train find the right track. Count each railroad tie. Color the track with 10 railroad ties red.

All Aboard

Color each train car with 8 barrels red.
Color each train car with 9 barrels blue.
Color each train car with 10 barrels green.

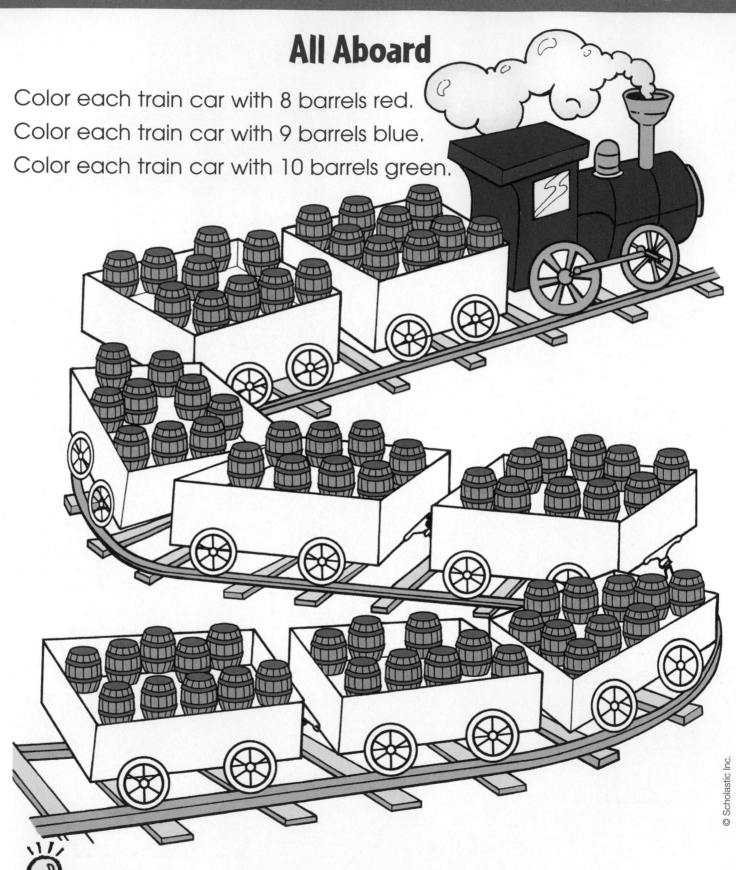

On another sheet of paper, draw a train with 10 train cars.

1, 2 . . . Presents for You

Draw a circle around each group of 1.

Draw a square around each group of 2.

3, 4 . . . Let's Read More!

Draw a triangle around each group of 3.

Draw a diamond around each group of 4.

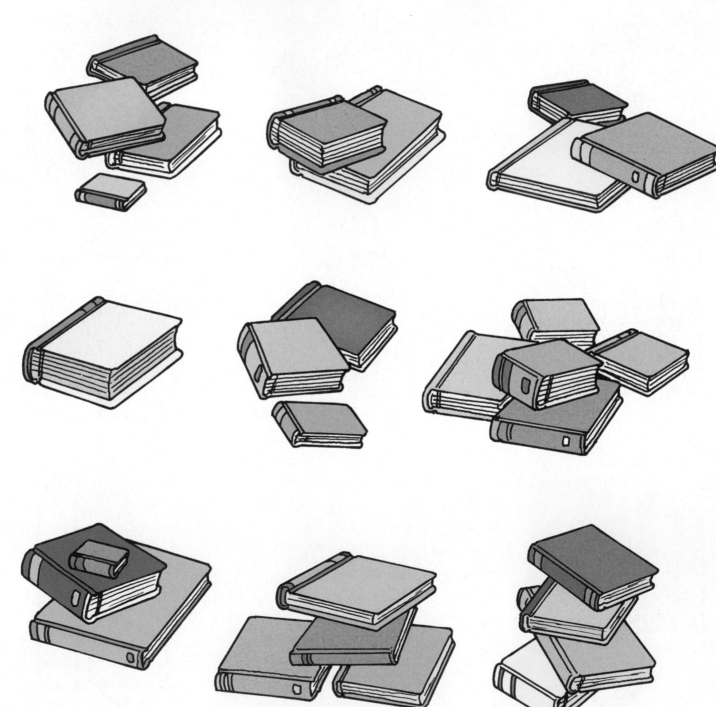

5, 6 ... Flowers to Pick

Draw an oval around each group of 5.

Draw a rectangle around each group of 6.

7, 8 . . . Time to Skate

Color each group of 7 red.
Color each group of 8 yellow.

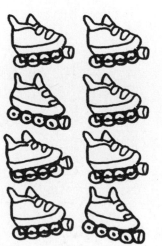

© Scholastic Inc.

9, 10 . . . It's Fun to Win!

Color each group of 9 blue.

Color each group of 10 green

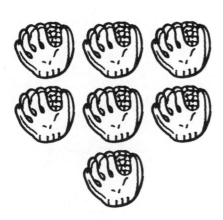

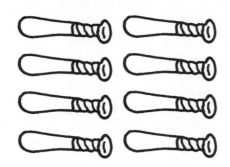

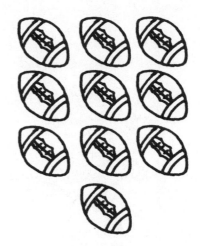

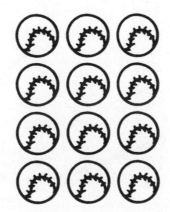

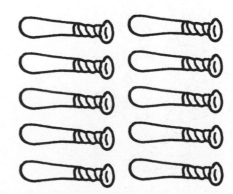

Bunny Number Fun

Color.

1 = pink   2 = green   3 = blue
4 = red   5 = brown   6 = yellow
7 = purple   8 = black   9 = orange

© Scholastic Inc.

A Colorful Garden

•	yellow	:	pink	⠃	red
⠿	black	⠯	orange	⠳	purple
⠻	blue	⠿⠿	green	⠿⠿	brown

Gumball Goodies

Color.

∴	blue	⦂∴	red	⦂⦂	green
⦂∴	orange	⦙⦙	purple	⦙⦚	black
⦙⦙⦙	brown	⦙⦙⦙	white	⦙⦙⦙	yellow

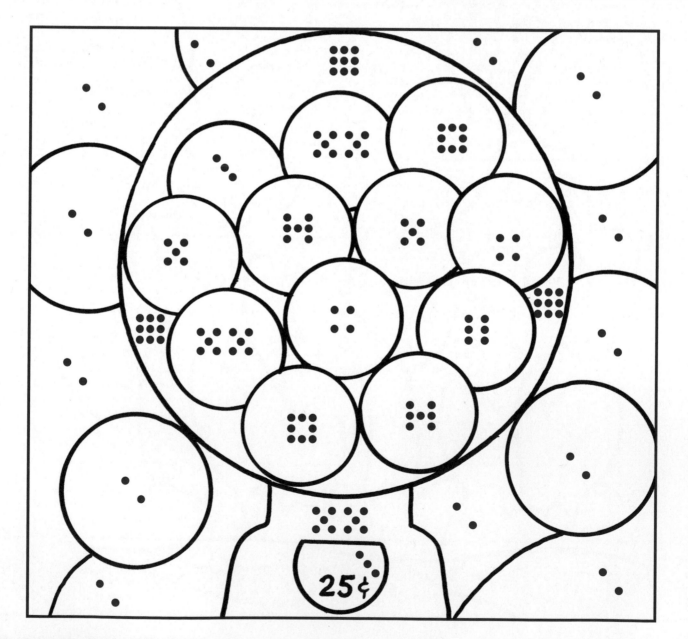

25¢

Count and Color

Color the correct number of objects.

1	
6	
4	
10	
5	
2	
7	
8	
3	
9	

Calling All Alarms

Help the fire truck get to the fire. Color the path that goes in order from **1** to **10**.

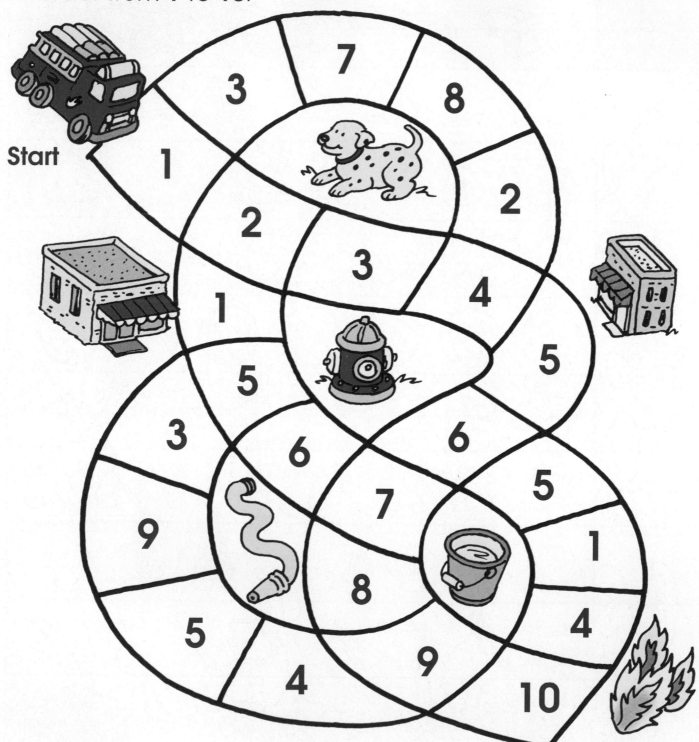

Eleven Excited Earthworms

Trace and write.

Color each set of 11 earthworms.

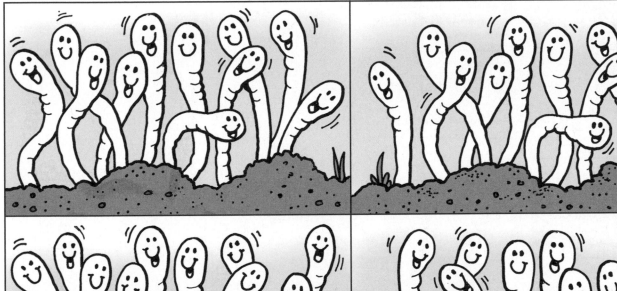

Betty Bookworm

Count each stack of books. Draw a line to match each stack to the correct number.

10

11

9

7

8

Color the stack with 11 books.

© Scholastic Inc.

Twelve Tasty Treats

Trace and write.

12

Count the candy in each jar. Color each jar with 12.

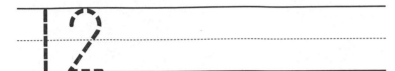

Gingerbread Man

Help the Gingerbread Man find his gingerbread house.
Color the path that goes in order from 1 to 12.

Count the lollipops in the picture. Draw more lollipops to make 12.

Thirteen Tasty Bones

Trace and write.

13

Circle 13 bones in each picture.

Draw more bones to make 13.

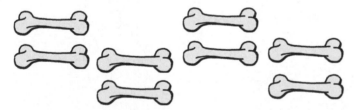

Count the bones. Circle the correct number.   12   13   14

Where, Oh Where, Has My Puppy Gone?

Help the puppy find its home. Trace the path that goes in order from 1 to 13.

Write the number that comes next in each bone.

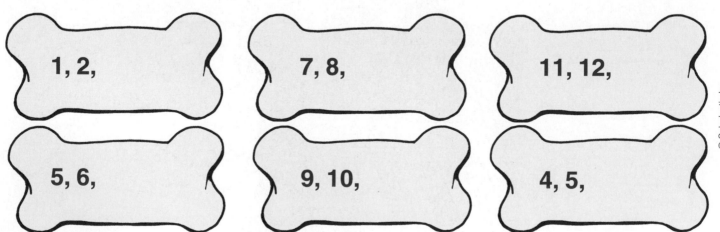

1, 2,

7, 8,

11, 12,

5, 6,

9, 10,

4, 5,

Juggling Fourteen Balls

Trace and write.

14

Color each ball with 14 dots.

Catch the Ball!

Count. Write how many.

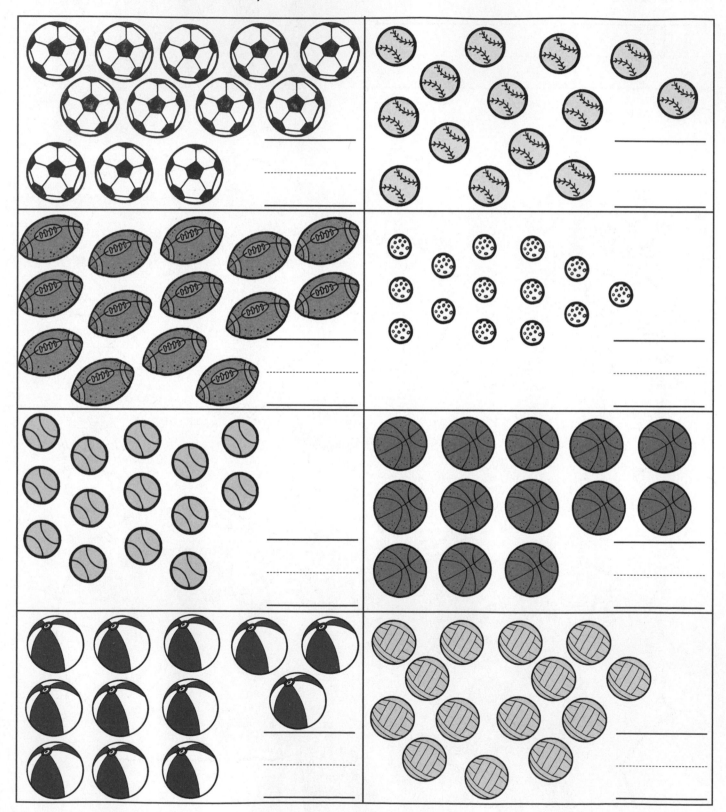

Fifteen Pennies

Trace and write.

15

Count the pennies in each bank. Color each bank with 15.

A Penny in Your Pocket

A penny equals 1¢. Count the pennies in each pocket.
Write the total.

_____ ¢

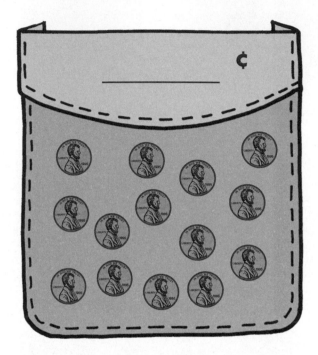

_____ ¢

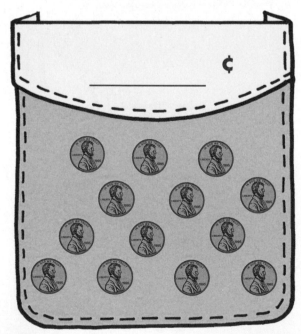

_____ ¢

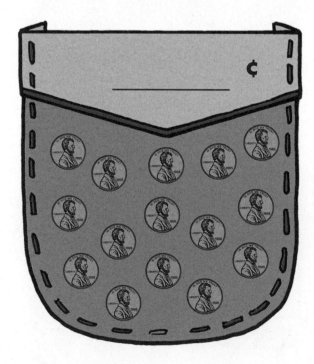

_____ ¢

 Find 15 pennies at home. Count them as you put them in your bank.

Sixteen Kites

Trace and write.

16

Count the bows on each tail. Color each kite
with 16 bows.

Flying High

Connect the dots from 1 to 16. Color the picture.

16

15

14

13

12

11

5

7

8

9

1

2

6

3

4

10

Count. Write how many.

Seventeen Gallons of Gas

Trace and write.

Find the gas pump by following the numbers in order from 1 to 17.

Way to Go!

Count. Write how many.

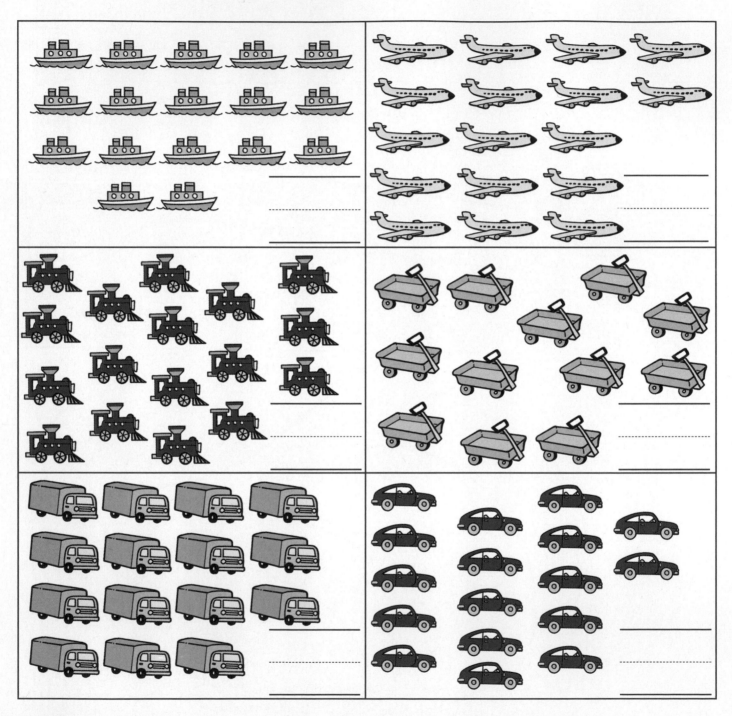

 On another sheet of paper, draw a train with 17 cars.

Eighteen Stars

Trace and write.

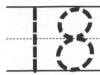

Circle 18 stars in each picture.

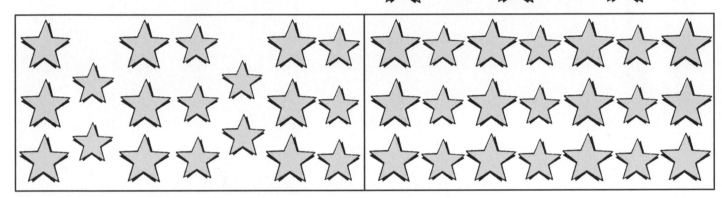

Draw more stars to make 18.

Count the planets. Write the number. _____

Out of This World

Count. Write how many. Color each group of 18 objects.

Nineteen Marbles

Trace and write.

I9

Circle the number that tells how many. Color each group with 19 marbles.

17   18   19

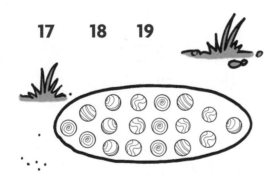

17   18   19

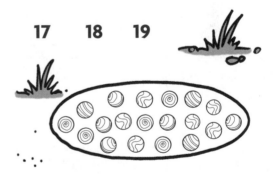

17   18   19

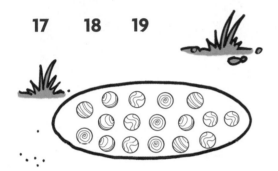

17   18   19

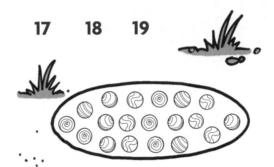

17   18   19

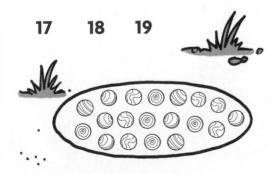

17   18   19

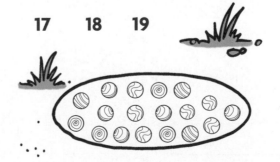

Let's Play Marbles

Circle 19 marbles.

Draw more marbles to make 19.

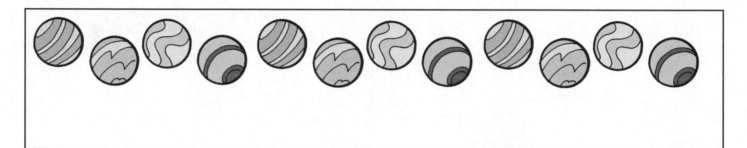

Count the marbles. Write the number.

Twenty Butterflies to Count

Trace and write.

20

Write the numbers 1 to 20 on the trail.

Start

Find and color 20 butterflies in the picture.

© Scholastic Inc.

Don't Bug Me!

Count each group of bugs. Draw a line to the matching number.

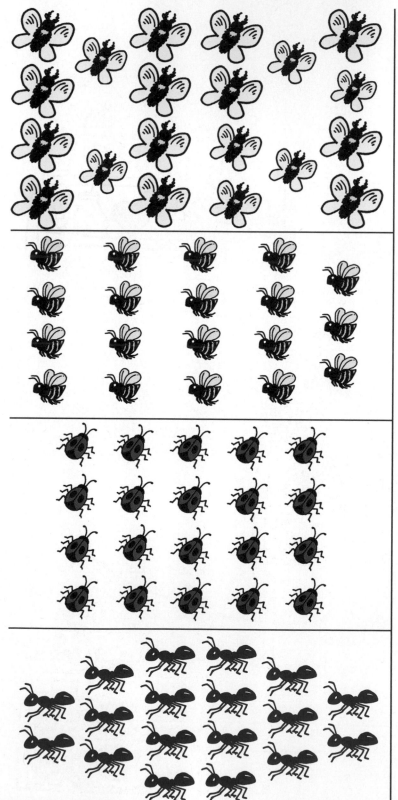

19

20

18

20

11, 12 . . . It's on the Shelf!

Draw a circle around each group of 11.

Draw a square around each group of 12.

13, 14 ... Let's Play the Tambourine!

Draw an oval around each group of 13.

Draw a rectangle around each group of 14.

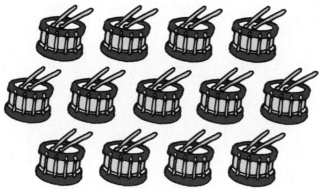

15, 16 . . . Eat Each Green Bean!

Draw a circle around each group of 15.

Draw a rectangle around each group of 16.

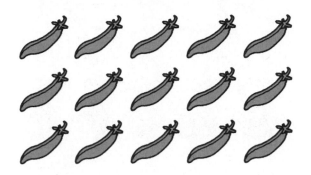

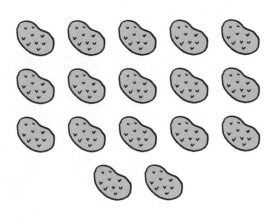

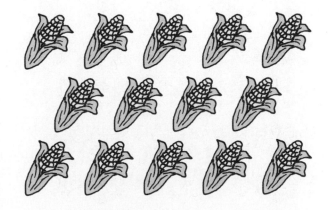

17, 18 . . . Don't Forget the Sunscreen!

Draw a circle around each group of 17.
Draw a square around each group of 18.

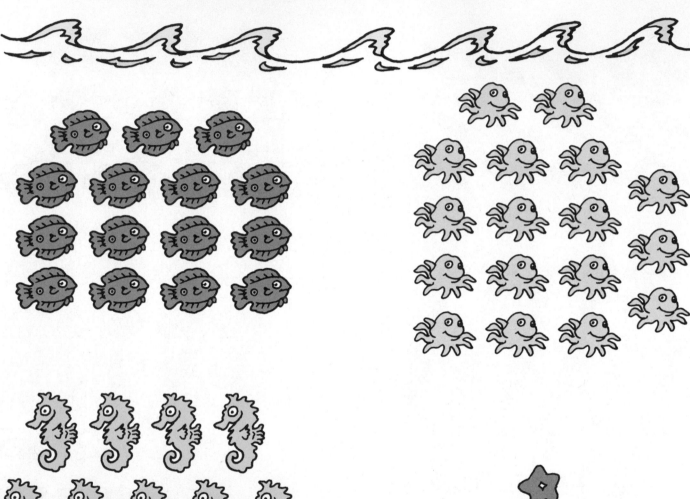

19, 20 . . . There Are Plenty!

Draw a circle around each group of 19.

Draw a square around each group of 20.

Time to Build

Color.
11 = yellow   12 = black   13 = blue
14 = white   15 = orange   16 = green
17 = red   18 = purple   19 = brown
20 = pink

Let's Count!

Color the correct number of objects.

14	
12	
16	
11	
18	
15	
17	
13	

Fun Fruits

Match.

13

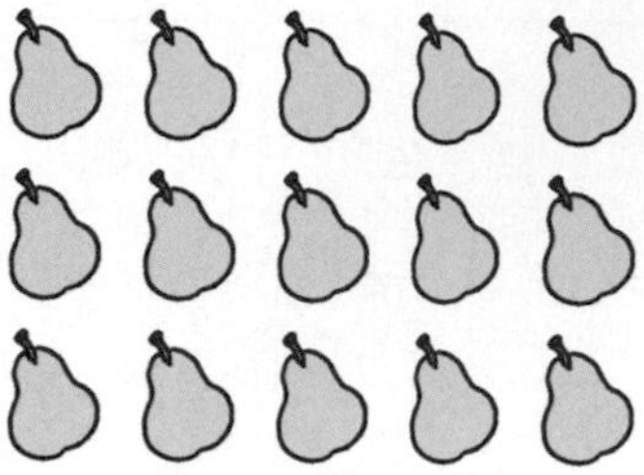

14

15

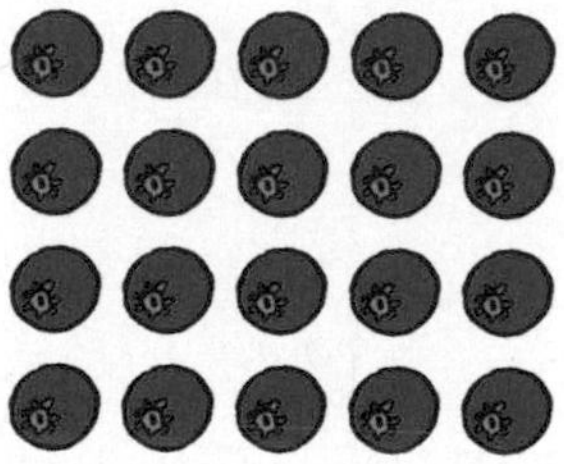

16

17

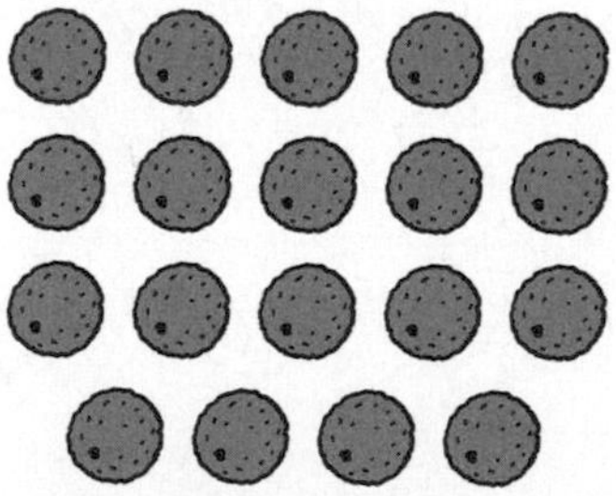

18

19

20

Flying High

Color the bows on the tails to match the number above each kite.

Juggling Act

Write each missing number.

Each Number in Its Spot

Write each missing number.

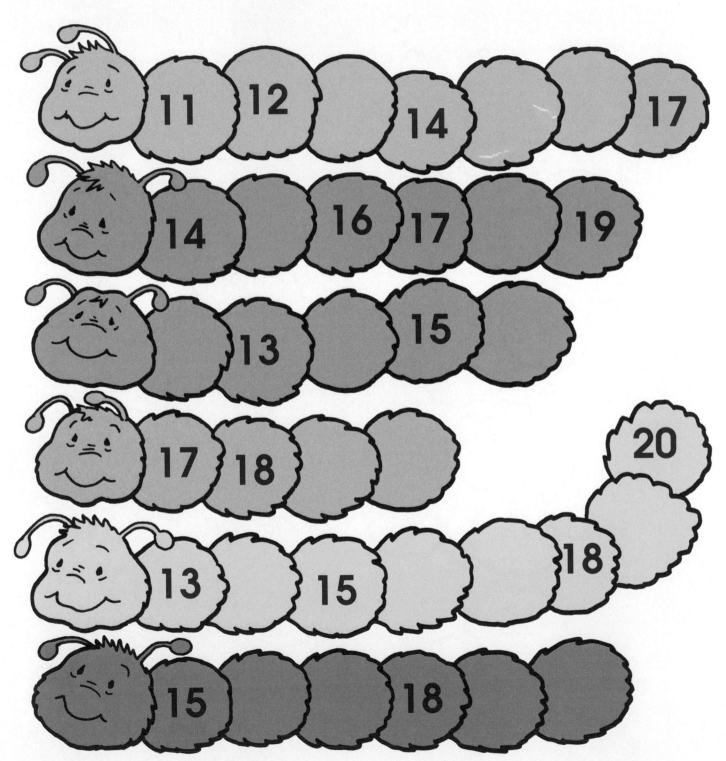

Pick Up Trash!

Help the trash collector find his way to the trash can.
Color a path in order from **1** to **20**.

Start

© Scholastic Inc.

Look Alikes

Color the pictures with the same number as in the
first picture.

Just the Same

Match the groups with the same number.

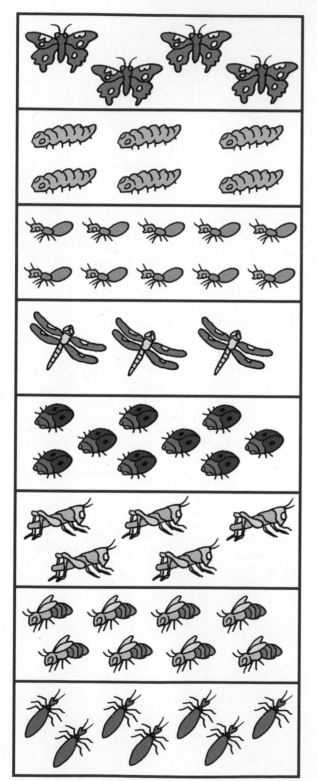

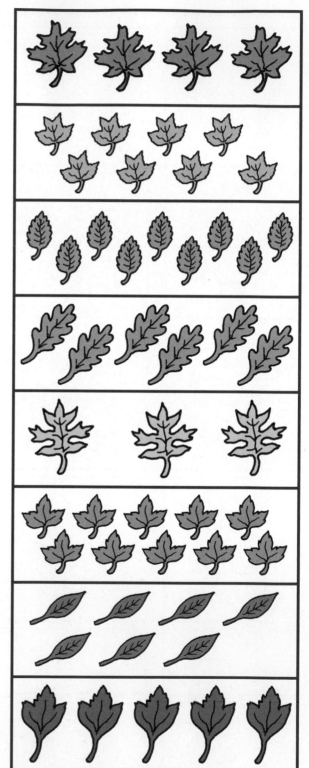

Tasty Treats

Circle the one with more.

A Little Snack

Circle the one with less.

Sweet Spotted Buddies

Color the dog with more spots in each picture.

Moving Along

Look at the picture.

Write the number.

How many?

| ☐ | ✈ | ☐ | 🚚 | ☐ | 🚐 |

| ☐ | 🚗 | ☐ | 🚁 | ☐ | 🚲 |

How many in all?

✈ and 🚗 ☐ 🚚 and ✈ ☐

🚐 and 🚲 ☐ 🚐 and 🚁 ☐

🚗 and 🚚 ☐ 🚁 and ✈ ☐

A Perfect Day at the Park

Circle how many you see in the picture.

🚲	1	5
🪑	4	2
🌼	8	5
🛝	6	3
🌳	7	10
🐕	2	8
🐦	9	7
🐿️	10	7
🛴	3	1

Circle how many you see in all.

🐦	+	🚲	=	8	9	10
🌼	+	🛝	=	3	8	9
🪑	+	🐕	=	6	2	4

Easy as One, Two, Three

Color.

one = yellow	**two** = black	**three** = blue
four = white	**five** = orange	**six** = green
seven = red	**eight** = purple	**nine** = brown
ten = pink		

Busy Bees

Count the bees in each picture.
Circle the correct number word.

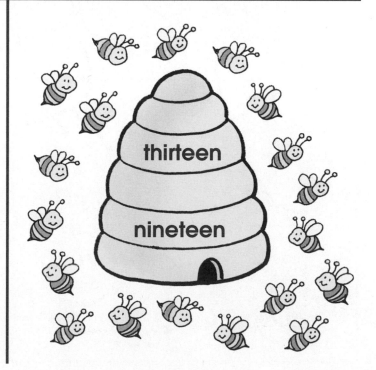

Lovely, Little Ladybugs

Count the spots on each picture.
Circle the correct number word.

	one **five**		**two** **seven**
	fourteen **sixteen**		**nineteen** **fifteen**
	ten **eleven**		**twenty** **twelve**
	eighteen **thirteen**		**nine** **eight**
	seven **four**		**seven** **three**

© Scholastic Inc.

Scholastic Success With

HANDWRITING

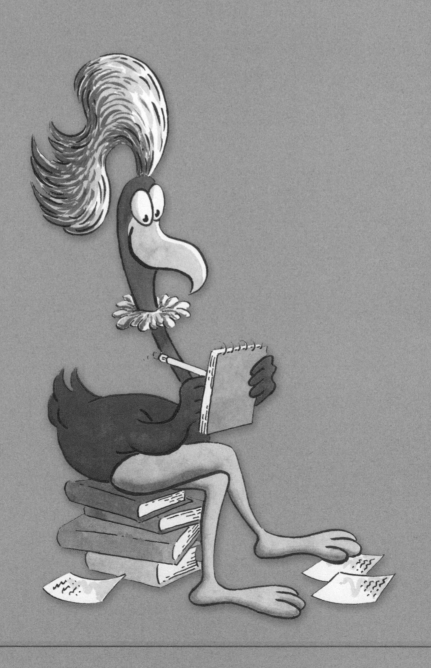

Petting–Zoo Pairs

Trace each line from a baby animal to its mother.

A Rainy Day

Trace each line from top to bottom.

Pretty Ponies

Trace each line from a pony to its child.

Big Balloons

Trace each line from bottom to top.

Balloons
50¢

Out Comes the Sun

Trace each line from top to bottom.

Colorful Kites

Trace each line from bottom to top.

Blowing Bubbles

Trace each circle. Start at the ●. Follow the ⟶ .

Clowning Around

Trace each circle. Start at the ●. Follow the ➞.

Wonderful Watermelons

Trace each curved line. Start at the ●. Follow the →.

Fun at the Fair

Trace each line. Start at the ●. Follow the ➡.

Lots of Licks

Trace and write.

Ticket Time

Trace and write.

 If the weather is nice, go outside and draw straight lines on a sidewalk with large pieces of chalk.

© Scholastic Inc.

Ooh! Aah!

Trace and write.

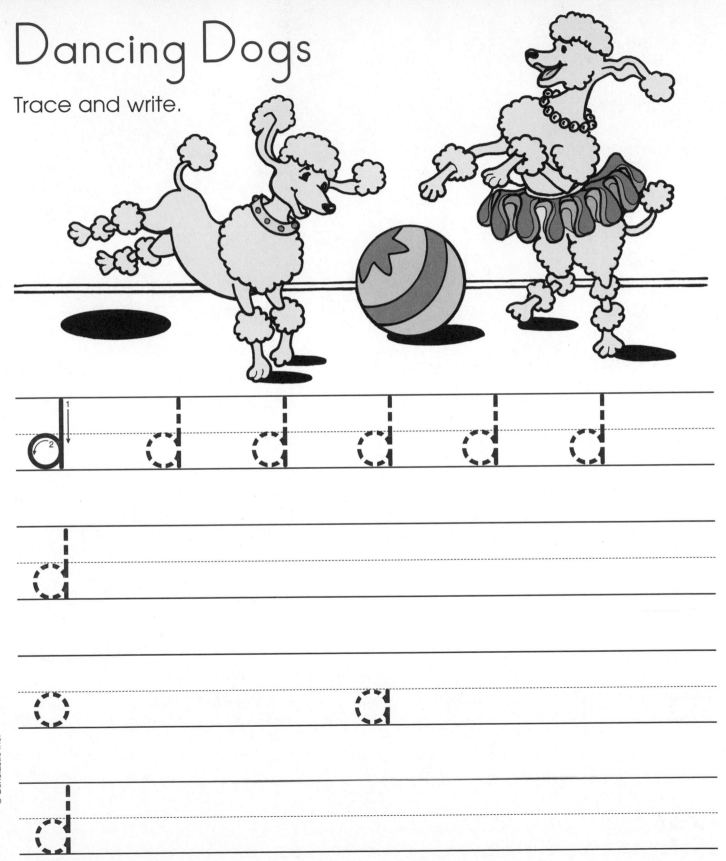

Dancing Dogs

Trace and write.

Crack! Splat!

Trace and write.

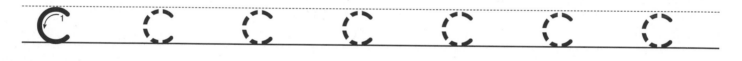

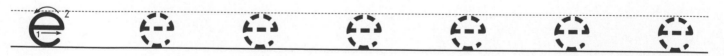

Fancy Fireworks

Trace and write.

f f f f f f f

f

c   c

f

Spray some shaving cream on cookie sheets. Spread out the shaving cream with your hands and use your pointer finger to draw letters in it.

Radiant Rainbow

Trace and write.

u u u u u u u

u

r r r r r r r

r

Time for a Nap

Trace and write.

n n n n n n n n

n

u   r

n

💡 **Go outside and practice writing letters in the sand or dirt with craft sticks.**

Bouncing Balls

Trace and write.

3 Bounces
25¢

b b b b b b

b

h h h h h h h

h

Perfect Pumpkins

Trace and write.

P P P P P P

p

b   h

Fill plastic squeeze-type bottles with different colors of tempera paint. Squeeze the paint onto construction paper to create letters.

p

Jumping Goats

Trace and write.

g g g g g g

g

j j j j j j j

j

A Quarter a Quack

Trace and write.

QUACKING DUCKS • 25¢ EACH

q q q q q q

q

g   j

q

💡 **Print large letters on pieces of paper. Press your thumb on an inkpad. Trace over the letters on the paper by stamping on your thumbprint.**

Music Makers

Trace and write.

m   m   m   m   m   m   m

m

S   S   S   S   S   S   S

S

m   s

A Vulture's Yo-Yo

Trace and write.

What Time Is It?

Trace and write.

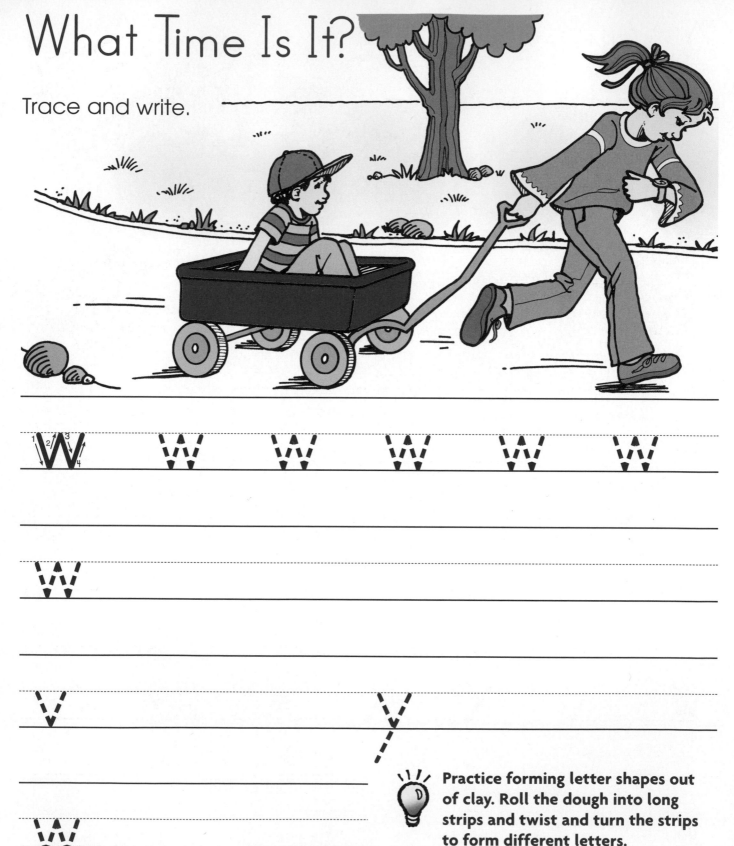

W W W W W W

W

V Y

💡 **Practice forming letter shapes out of clay. Roll the dough into long strips and twist and turn the strips to form different letters.**

W

Box Kites

Trace and write.

K K K K K K K

k

X X X X X X X

x

Zooming Along

Trace and write.

Z Z Z Z Z Z Z

Z

K   X

© Scholastic Inc.

Z

 Practice forming letters using craft sticks. Glue your stick letters to construction paper.

Ice-Cold Lemonade

Trace and write.

Toot-Toot!

Trace and write.

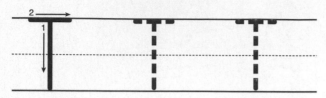

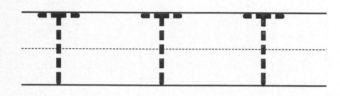

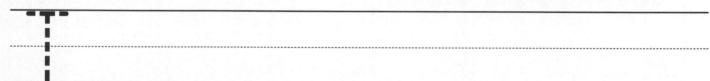

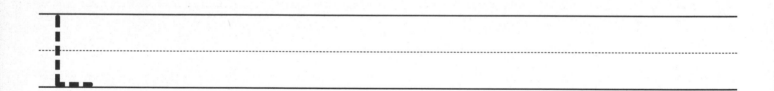

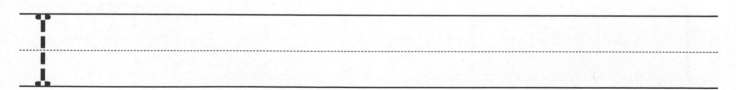

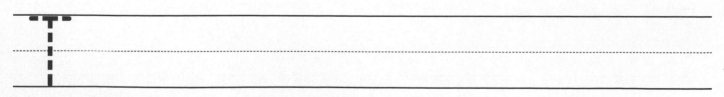

Making Friends at the Fair

Trace and write.

Hungry for Hot Dogs

Trace and write.

A Cozy Quilt

Trace and write.

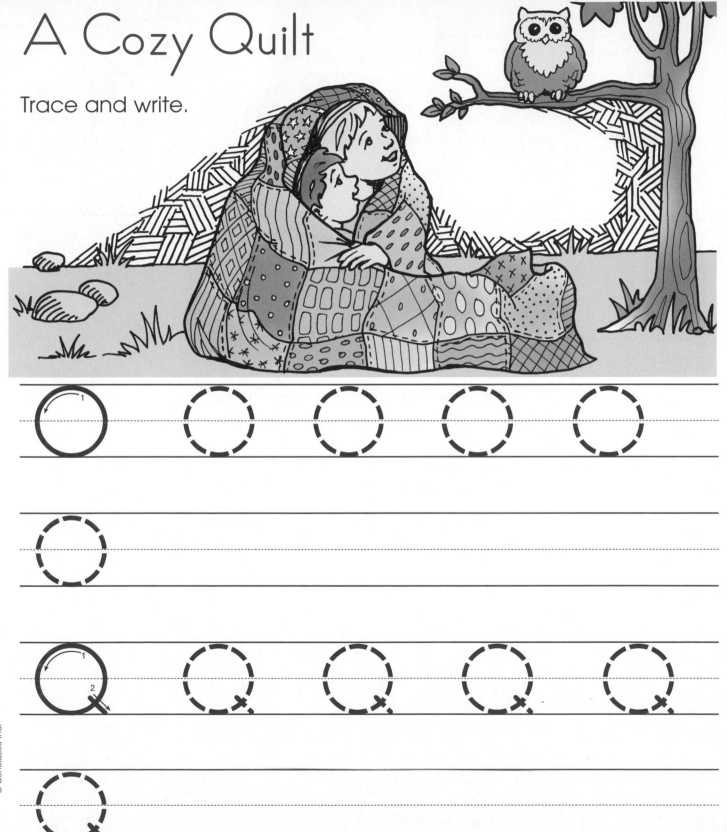

Cotton Candy

Trace and write.

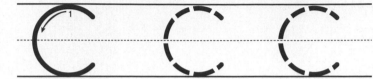

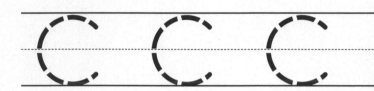

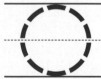

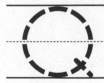

The Dunking Booth

Trace and write.

DUNK ME! $1.00

2 THROWS $1.00

B B B B B B B

B

D D D D D D D

D

Feeding Time

Trace and write.

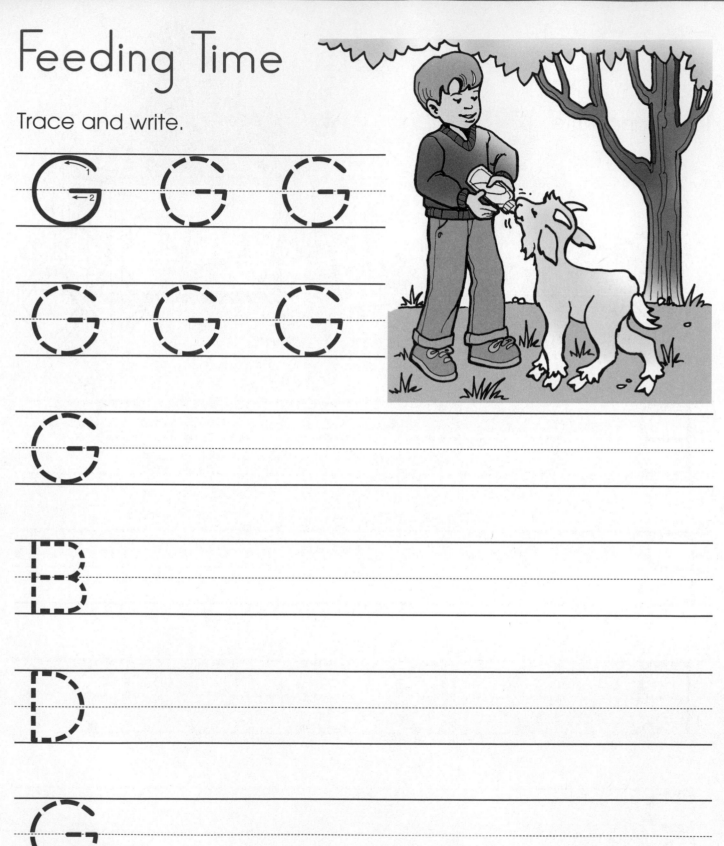

G G G

G G G

G

B

D

G

Rolling Roller Coaster

Trace and write.

P P P P P P P

P

R R R R R R R

R

Up, Up, and Away!

Trace and write.

U U U U

U U U U

U U U U

P

R

U

Sack-Jumping

Trace and write.

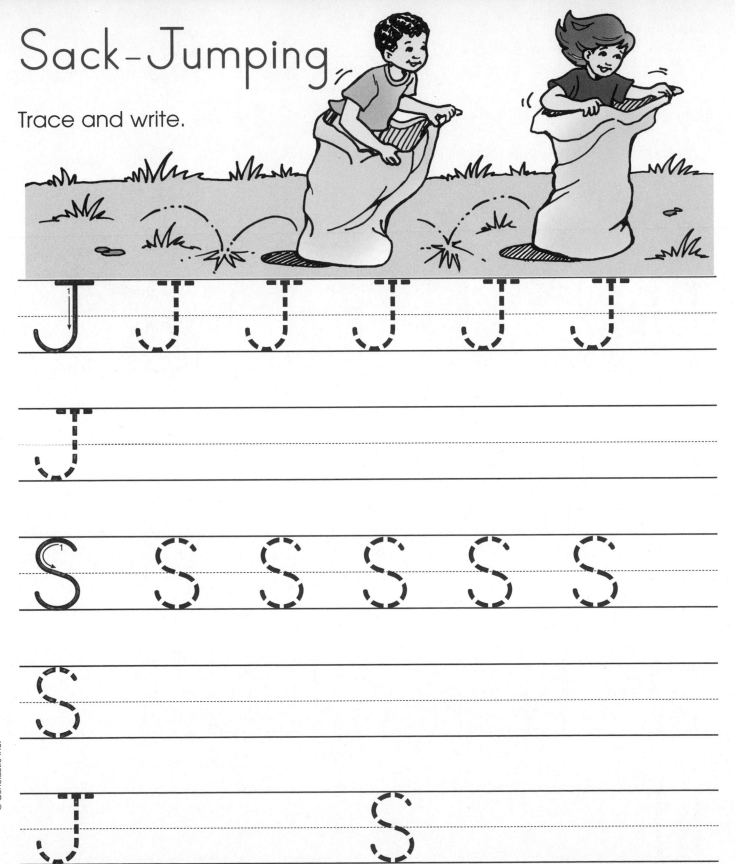

J J J J J J

J

S S S S S S

S

J   S

Ant Antics

Trace and write.

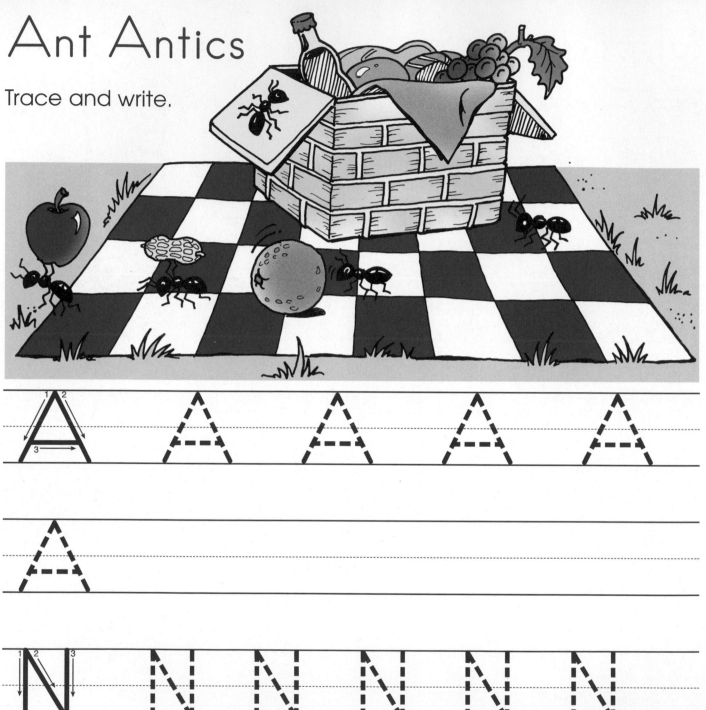

Merrily We Go Around!

Trace and write.

M M M M

M M M M

M

A

N

M

What a Day!

Trace and write.

A Youthful Yawn

Trace and write.

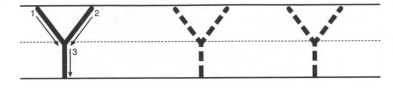

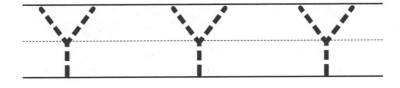

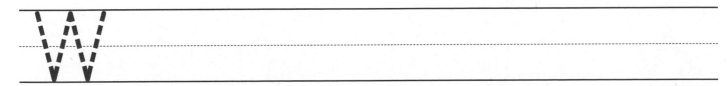

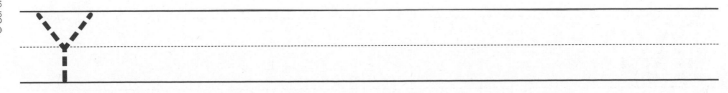

Can We Keep One?

Trace and write.

Free to good Home

K K K K K K K K

K

X X X X X X

X

The Petting Zoo

Trace and write.

Z Z Z

Z Z Z

Z

K

X

Z

A–Z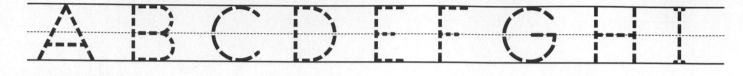

Trace and write.

A B C D E F G H I

_____

J K L M N O P Q

_____

R S T U V W X Y Z

_____

a–z

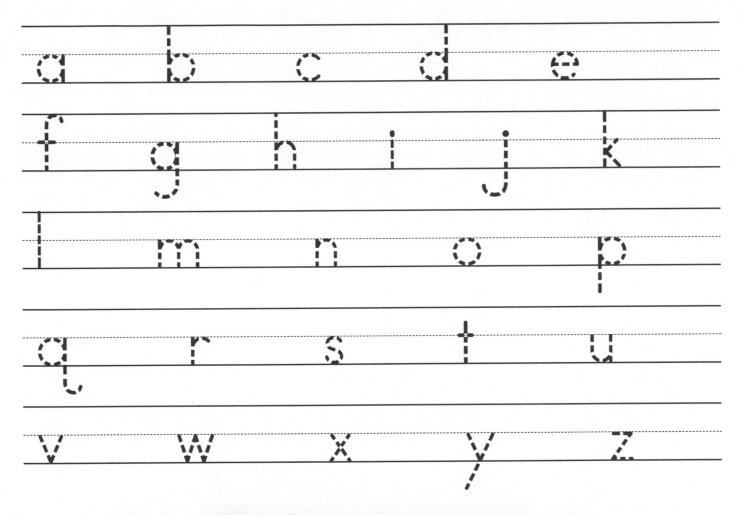

Trace and write.

a b c d e

f g h i j k

l m n o p

q r s t u

v w x y z

abcd

1–5

Trace and write.

6-10

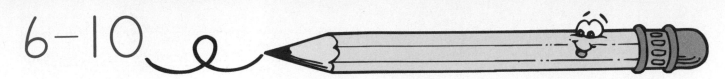

Trace and write.

Color Words

Trace and write.

red

yellow

blue

green

orange

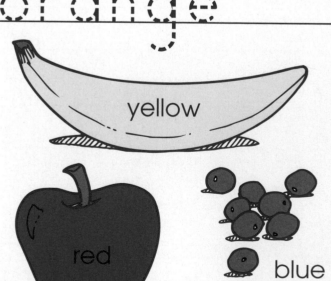

yellow

red

blue

green

orange

More Color Words

Trace and write.

purple

brown

black

white

pink

pink

purple

brown

black

white

Number Words

Trace and write.

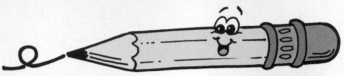

1 one

2 two

3 three

4 four

5 five

More Number Words

Trace and write.

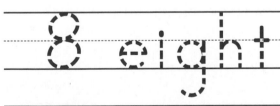

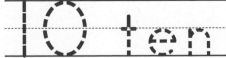

Shapes

Trace and write.

oval

heart

circle

square

triangle

diamond

rectangle

Days of the Week

Trace and write.

Sunday

Monday

Tuesday

Wednesday

Thursday

Friday

Saturday

Months

Jan. Feb. March April May June

Trace and write.

January

February

March

April

May

June

Months

Trace and write.

July

August

September

October

November

December

Practice writing words.

Scholastic Success With

BASIC CONCEPTS

Coloring Crayons

Color each crayon to show its color.
Draw a line from each crayon to its matching color word.

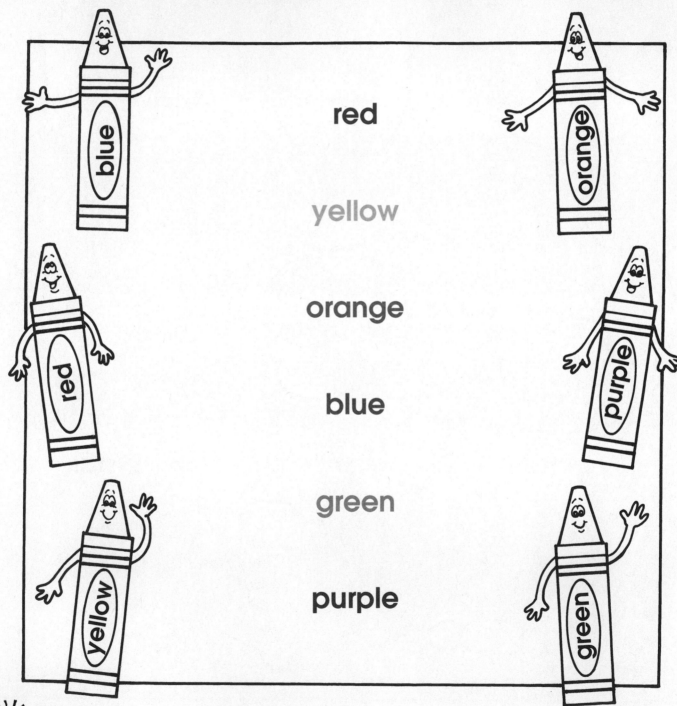

red

yellow

orange

blue

green

purple

💡 **Name three things that are red.**

What Color Am I?

Say the color words. Color the pictures.

yellow

red

green

blue

orange

black

purple

brown

💡 **On another sheet of paper, draw four things that are green.**

Color Train

Draw a line to match each picture to the correct color. Color.

Color Train

Draw a line to match each picture to the correct color. Color.

Rolling Through the Hills

Color.

Sorting Shapes

This is a **circle** ◯ . This is a **square** ▢ . A square has four sides that are the same length. This is a **rectangle** ▭ . A rectangle also has four sides. The opposite sides of a rectangle are the same length. This is a **triangle** △ . A triangle has three sides.

Color the circles 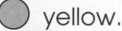 yellow.
Color the squares  red.
Color the triangles 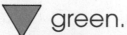 green.
Color the rectangles blue.

Circle and Square Search

Color each circle shape.

Color each square shape.

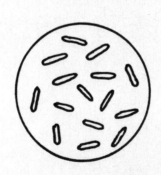

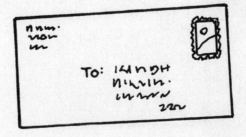

Rectangle and Triangle Teasers

Color each rectangle shape.

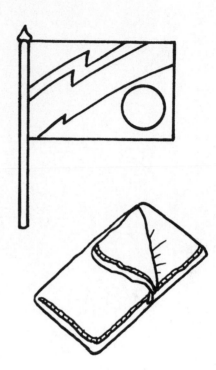

Color each triangle shape.

Oval and Diamond Detectives

Color each diamond shape.

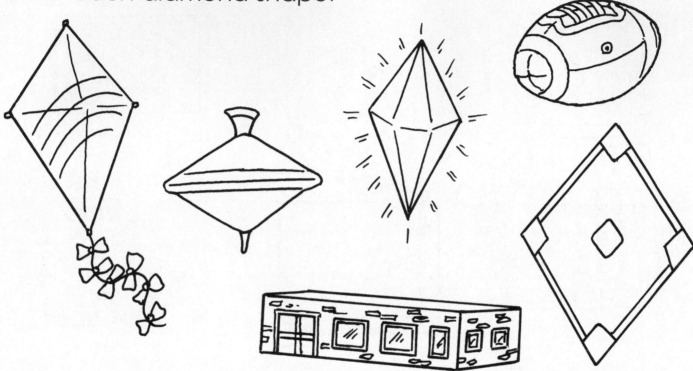

Color each oval shape.

Shape Match-Up

Trace each shape. Draw a line to match each object to its shape. Color.

square

circle

triangle

rectangle

To A FRIEND
123 SHAPES
ANYWHERE
45678

More Shape Match-Up

Trace each shape. Draw a line to match each object to its shape. Color.

Shape Teasers

Color each shape using the code.

 = red = blue = green = yellow

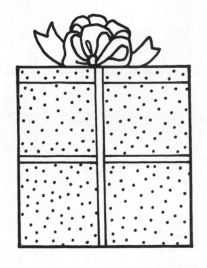

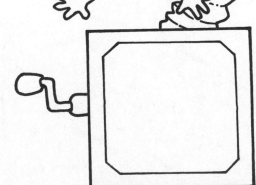

 Name something else with each shape.

Zany Zoo Shapes

Color. 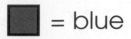 = black 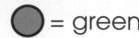 = blue  = red

 = brown = green = yellow

© Scholastic Inc.

Smiling Shapes

Draw a line to the shape that comes next.

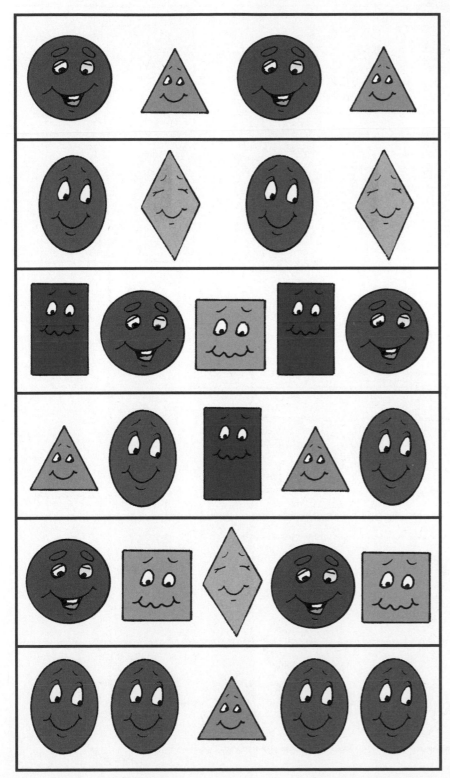

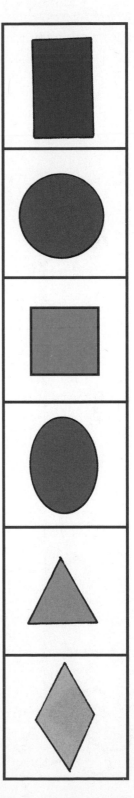

What Comes Next?

Circle what comes next.

Ordering Outfits

Circle what comes next.

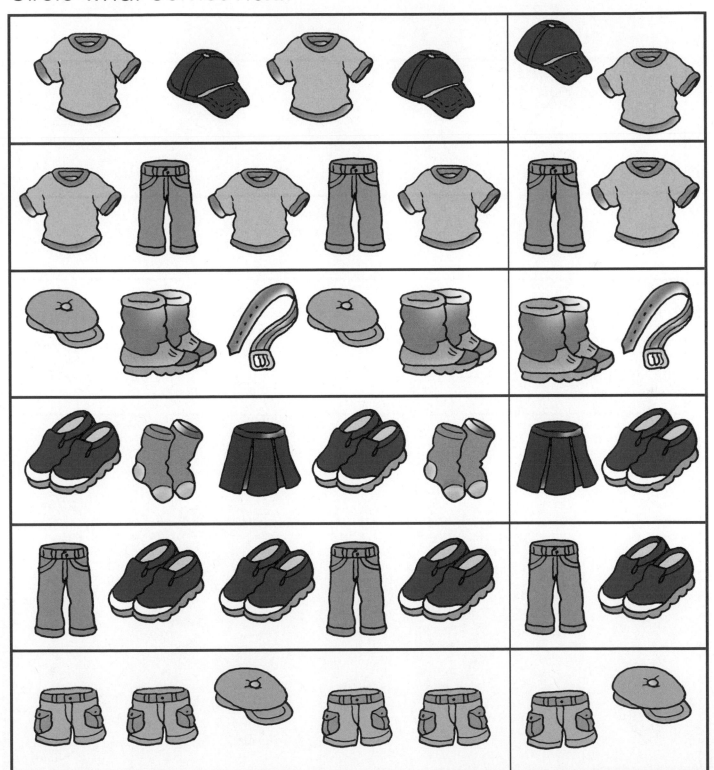

Decorate a Headband

Draw the shapes that finish the patterns. Then color your headband.

You Can Draw an Apple!

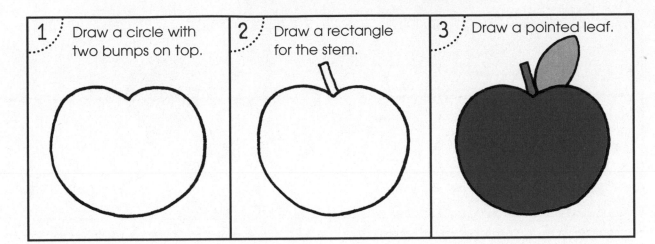

1 Draw a circle with two bumps on top.

2 Draw a rectangle for the stem.

3 Draw a pointed leaf.

You Can Draw a Balloon!

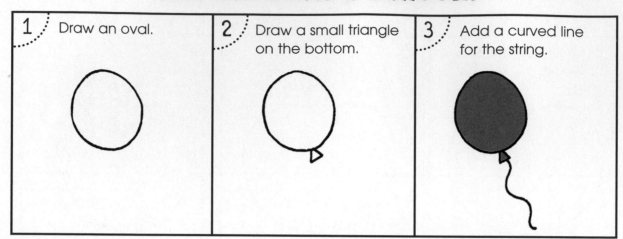

1 Draw an oval.

2 Draw a small triangle on the bottom.

3 Add a curved line for the string.

You Can Draw a Kite!

1 Draw a diamond.	**2** Draw a line from the top to the bottom.	**3** Draw a line from left to right.
4 Draw a curvy line for the string.	**5** Draw 2 small triangles on the left side of the string.	**6** Draw 2 small triangles on the right side of the string.

Everything in Order

The **sequence** is the order in which things happen.

Write 1 under the picture that happens first.
Write 2 under the picture that happens second.

_____

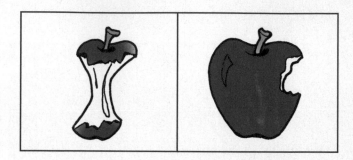

_____

_____

_____

_____

_____

 What do you do first when you wake up?

First Things First

Write 1 by what happened first.

Write 2 by what happened second.

Write 3 by what happened third.

Perfect Order

Write 1 by what happened first.
Write 2 by what happened second.
Write 3 by what happened third.

Out of Place

Say the things in the pictures. Circle two things in each picture that do not belong. Color the pictures.

penguin

chest

swing

window

bed

rug

toys

stove

sink

broom

table

chair

snowman

tulip

Where Do I Belong?

Draw a line to show where each thing belongs.

 On another sheet of paper, draw a picture of something else that might be on a farm.

© Scholastic Inc.

Going to School

Find and color these things in the picture.

 pencil

 scissors

book

paper

 glue

eraser

 Color one thing in the picture that does not belong.

Up, Down, and All Around

This mouse is **up**.  This mouse is **down**.

Color the animals that are up red.
Color the animals that are down blue.

💡 **How many animals are up?** _____
How many animals are down? _____

© Scholastic Inc.

Pretty Balloons

This is **high**.   This is **low**.

Color the high balloons purple.
Color the low balloons yellow.

 Circle the lowest balloon.

Up on Top

Draw a ⭕ around the on the **top**.

Draw a ⭕ around the on the **top**.

Draw a ⭕ around the on the **bottom**.

Draw a ⭕ around the on the **bottom**.

Above or Below . . . Sure You Know!

Draw a ☐ around the **above** the .

Draw a ☐ around the **above** the 🍃.

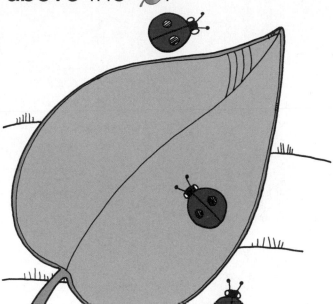

Draw a ☐ around the 🐰 **below** the .

Draw a ☐ around the  **below** the 🪑.

Quacky Business

This duck is **over**.   This duck is **under**.

Circle the correct answer.

Where do you see more ducks?   over   under

Where do you see more frogs?   over   under

 How many ducks are there altogether in the picture? _____

© Scholastic Inc.

In, Out, and All About

Color the animals that are **in** their houses.

More In, Out, and All About

This animal is **in**.    This animal is **out**.

Color each animal that is in its home.

Size It Up

Draw a ◇ around the picture that is **short**.

Draw a ◇ around the picture that is **long**.

Transportation Station

Draw a ⬜ around the picture that is **big**.

 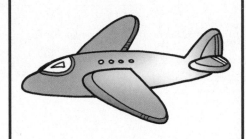 

Draw a ⬜ around the picture that is **small**.

Just the Right Size

This butterfly is **large**. This butterfly is **small**.
Circle the large item on each petal.

 Name two things that are larger than you.

Star Lights

This star is **right** of the moon. 🌙⭐

This star is **left** of the moon. ⭐🌙

Color each ⭐ that is right of the moon yellow.

Color each ⭐ that is left of the moon orange.

 How many stars do you see in all? _____

Mark the Map

Trace a 🤚 **L** or 🤚 **R** path in each picture.

How Do You Feel?

Sometimes you feel **happy**. Sometimes you feel **sad**.

Look at each picture. Draw a line to the happy or sad face to show how the picture makes you feel.

Tricks for Treats

Count. Circle the dog with **less** bones.

Time for a Picnic

The rabbit has **more** than the dog.
The dog has **less** than the rabbit.

Write how many. Circle the group that has **more**.

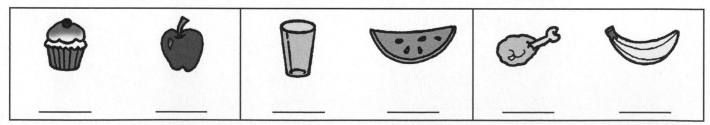

_____   _____   _____   _____   _____   _____

Write how many. Circle the group that has **less**.

_____   _____   _____   _____   _____   _____

What Is Really Real?

Things that are **pretend** are not **real**.

Color the real pictures.
Do not color the pretend pictures.

 Make up a story about a pretend trip to the moon. Tell your story to a grown-up.

A Silly City

Circle 5 pretend things in the picture.

Searching for Opposites

An elephant is big. A mouse is little.
Big and little are **opposites**.

Circle the picture that shows the opposite.

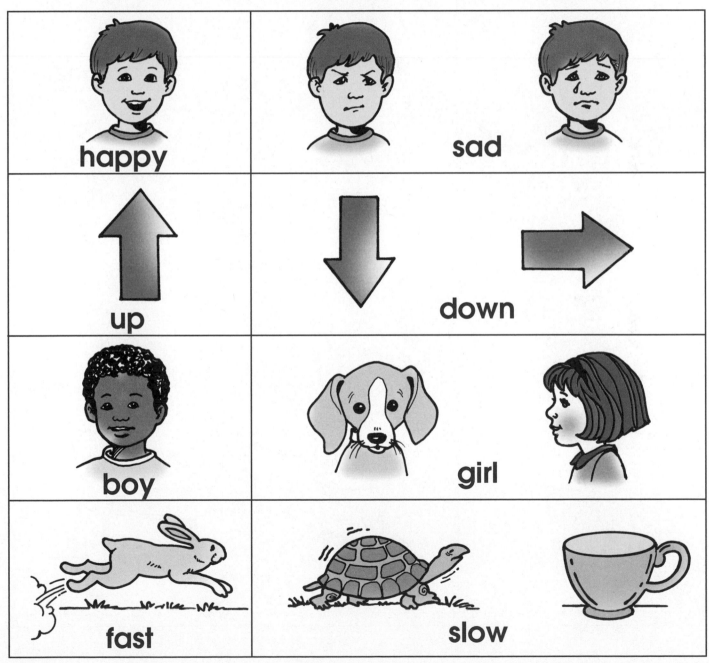

 Name something you can do fast. Name something you can do slow.

Searching for More Opposites

Circle the picture that shows the **opposite**.

big   little

in   out

hot   cold

full   empty

 On another sheet of paper, draw a picture of a something that might be larger than an elephant.

Different as Can Be

Follow the maze to match the pictures that show the opposite.

A Perfect Match

 and are the **same**.

Connect the cars that are the same.

 Name one way you and a friend are the same.

A Ride in the Clouds

 and are **different**.

Circle the plane that is different in each row.

 Name one way you and a friend are different.

Triangle Teasers

Draw a △ around the picture that is **different**.

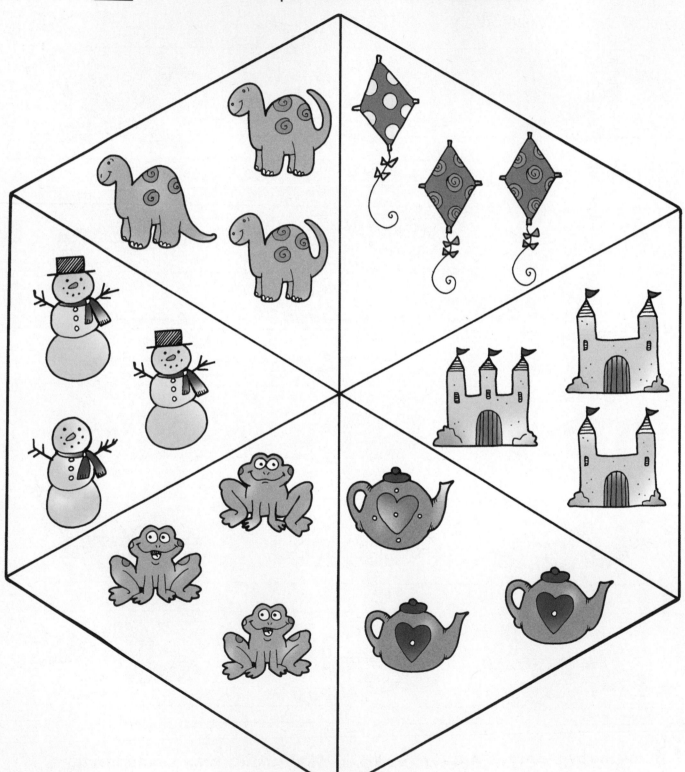

Small but Strong

This ant is **small**.

This ant is **smaller**.

This ant is **smallest**.

Put an **X** on the smallest animal in each row.

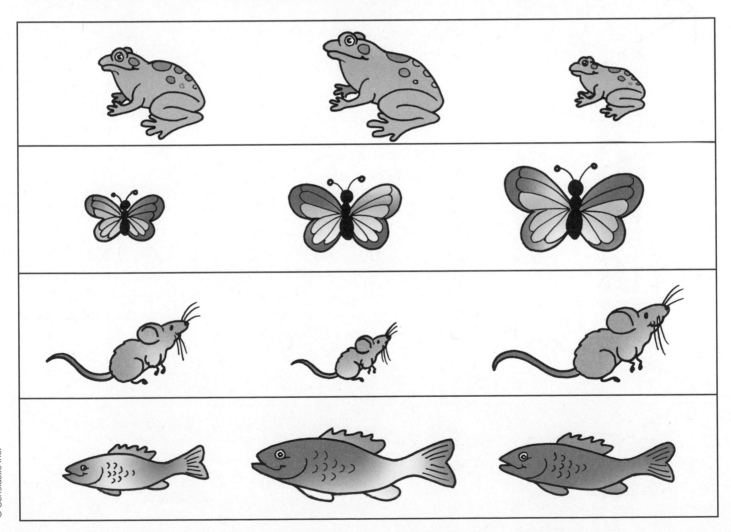

On another sheet of paper, draw something smaller than a watermelon.

Bigger and Better

This bear is **big**.	This bear is **bigger**.	This bear is **biggest**.

Draw a rectangle around the biggest animal in each row.

 On another sheet of paper, draw a picture of something bigger than a bear.

Side by Side

Draw a line to match the pictures that go together.

Out of Place

Put an **X** on the picture that does not belong.

Together Is Better

Color the picture that goes with the first picture in each row.

Special Helpers

Draw a line to match the workers to their tools.

I Want My Mommy!

Draw a line from each animal **baby** to its **mother**.

Circle the baby that hatches from an egg.

How Is the Weather?

What we can do outside each day depends on the **weather**.

Draw a line from each weather word to its picture.

sunny

windy

snowy

rainy

All Dressed Up

We wear **clothes** to go with the weather.
Connect the top, bottom, and shoes that go together.

 On another sheet of paper, draw a picture of you in your favorite clothes.

Special Helpers

Special people **work** each day to help others.

Match each worker to something the worker uses to help others.

 Think of three things you can do to help your family.

© Scholastic Inc.

Time to Work

People use **tools** to do work.

Color the tool in each row that the worker needs.

 Talk about what you want to be when you grow up.

Time to Travel

Transportation is how we get from one place to another.

Color the transportation for land green.
Color the transportation for water blue.
Color the transportation for air purple.

 Name all the kinds of transportation you have used.

Totally Amazing

The **body** is made up of many parts.
Draw a line to each body part.

eyes

hair

nose

leg

arm

foot

hand

chest

 Name three other body parts.

Sensational Senses

We use our **senses** to learn about new things.

We **see** with our .

We **hear** with our .

We **smell** with our .

We **taste** with our .

We **touch** with our 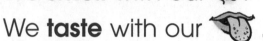.

Look at each picture. Circle the sense you would use.

© Scholastic Inc.

A Place to Call Home

Find the children's houses on the map. Then use the color words on their shirts to color the houses.

Say your address.

We Are Family

Write the names of each member of your family.
Sort them into the correct categories.

My Family

Adults

Children

Scholastic Success With

PHONICS

Hop to It!

Color the lily pad with the letter that matches the frog in each row. Then circle the picture that begins with that letter.

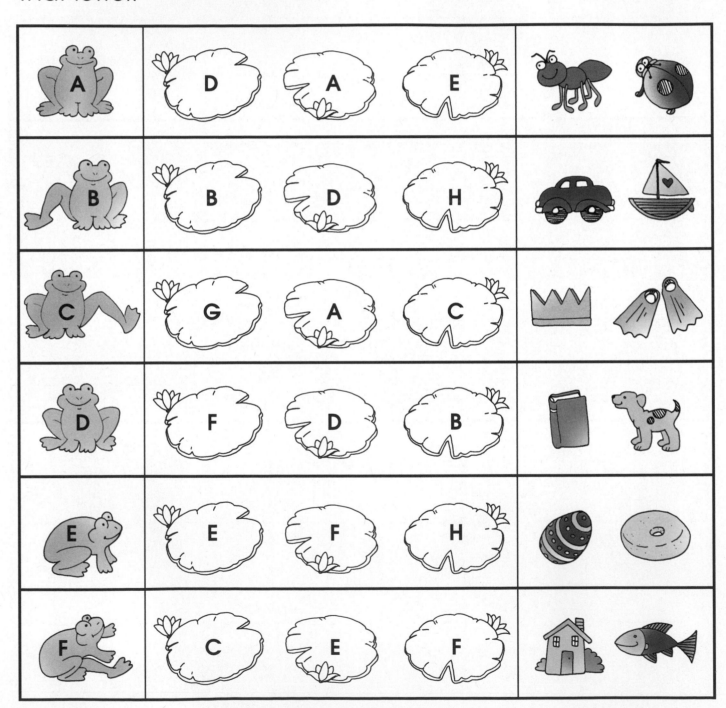

Hop to It!

Color the lily pad with the letter that matches the frog in each row. Then circle the picture that begins with that letter.

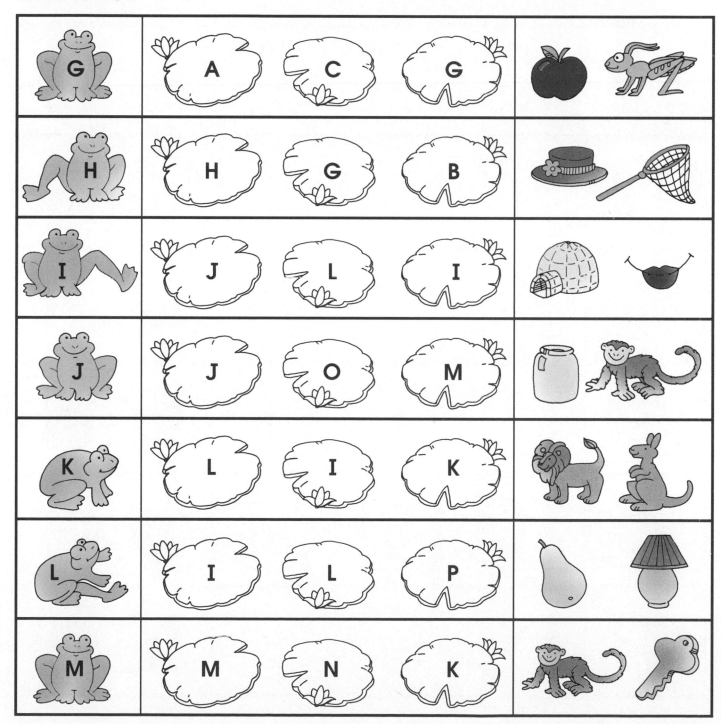

© Scholastic Inc.

Letter Flags

Color the carrot with the letter that matches the flag in each row. Then circle the picture that begins with that letter.

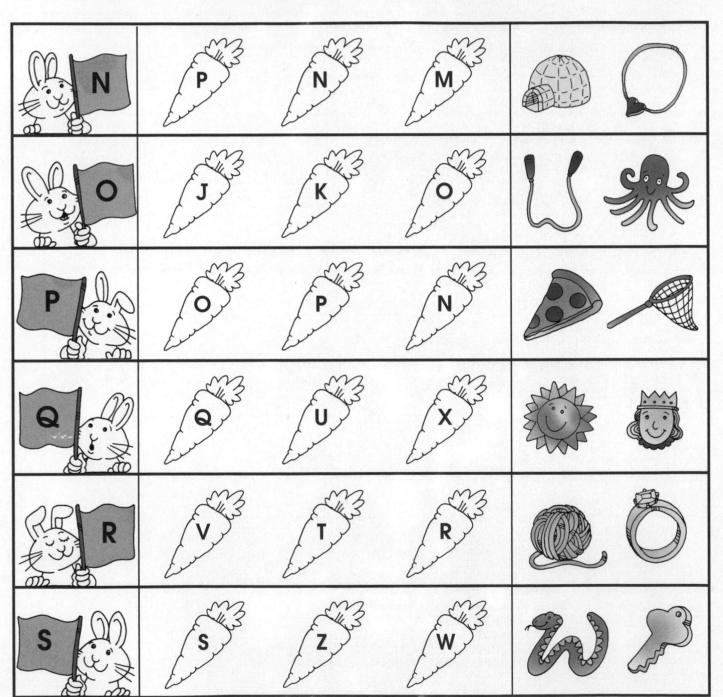

Letter Flags

Color the carrot with the letter that matches the flag
in each row. Then circle the picture that begins with
that letter.

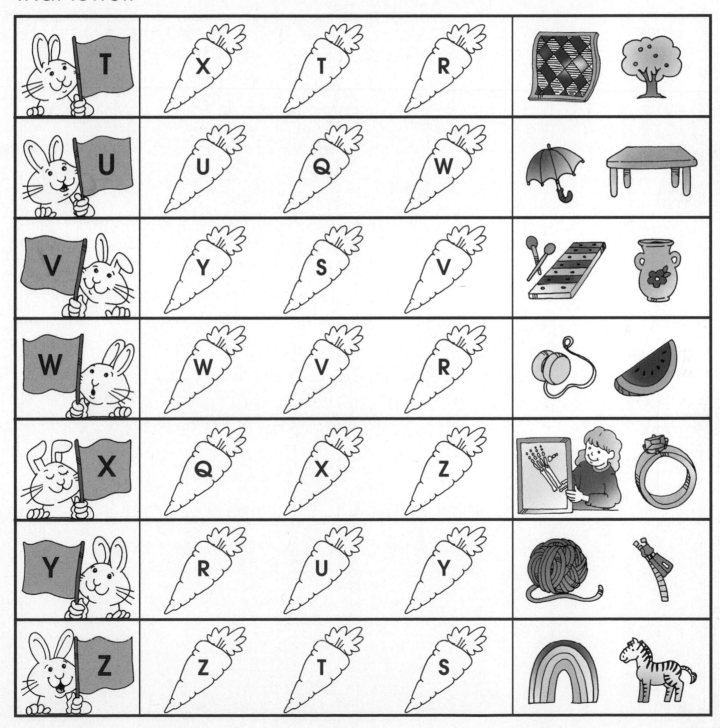

What Is a Consonant?

Can you say the alphabet? There are 26 letters in the alphabet. Five of the letters are vowels: *A, E, I, O,* and *U.*

All the rest are consonants.

Look at the alphabet below. Mark an **X** through the five vowels: *A, E, I, O,* and *U.* Now say the names of all the consonants.

A B C D E F G H I
J K L M N O P Q
R S T U V W X Y Z

How many consonants are there? _____

Color each balloon that has a consonant in it.

Bobby the Bear

 B *makes the sound you hear at the beginning of the words* **Bobby** *and* **bear**.

Bobby the bear is going shopping for things that begin with **b**. Help Bobby find ten things in this store that begin with **b**. Draw a circle around each one.

 What insect buzzes around flowers and makes honey? Draw it on another sheet of paper. Tell a friend what you know about this insect.

© Scholastic Inc.

Doctor Dave

 D *makes the sound you hear at the beginning of the words* **doctor** *and* **Dave**.

Look in Doctor Dave's bag. Color only the pictures that begin with **d**. Put an **X** on the pictures that do not begin with **d**.

 She is another kind of doctor. She works on your teeth. Her job begins with *d*. **Who is she? On another sheet of paper, draw yourself at her office.**

Fancy the Fish

F *makes the sound you hear at the beginning of the words* **fancy** *and* **fish**.

Fancy the fish is blowing bubbles. Draw a bubble around the pictures that begin with **f**. Put an **X** on the pictures that do not begin with **f**.

 This word begins with *f*. **It names a brave person who saves people when their houses are burning. Who is this person? On another sheet of paper, draw a picture of this person's truck.**

© Scholastic Inc.

Happy the Hippo

H *makes the sound you hear at the beginning of the words* **happy** *and* **hippo**.

Help Happy the hippo find the **h** words. Say the picture in each box. Color only the pictures that begin with **h**.

This game begins with *h*. One child counts to ten and then tries to find the other children. Do you know what it is? At playtime, play this game with your friends.

Joe the Janitor

 J *makes the sound you hear at the beginning of the words* **Joe** *and* **janitor**.

Help Joe the janitor find the **j** words. In each trash can, draw a box around two pictures that begin with **j**.

 What kind of candy begins with *j*, **looks like beans, and comes in lots of different colors? Say the answer. On another sheet of paper, draw a glass jar with 21 of these in it. Count carefully! Color them.**

Katie the Kangaroo

K _makes the sound you hear at the beginning of the words_ **Katie** _and_ **kangaroo**.

Help Katie the kangaroo find the pictures that begin with **k**. Color them in.

 This word begins with _k_**. It can mean a young goat, or it can mean a young person. It rhymes with** _lid_**. What is it?**

© Scholastic Inc.

Lazy the Lion

➡️ **L** *makes the sound you hear at the beginning of the words* **lazy** *and* **lion**.

Help Lazy the lion find a word that begins with **l** to match each picture. Circle the correct word.

lamp clock	zipper lace	tree leaf	ladder hoe
ladybug bee	lake town	dog lamb	hand leg
lightning snow	apple lemon	book letter	lettuce corn
nose lips	lizard goat	worm lobster	log rock

 This word begins with an *l*. It is a good feeling that you have about the people you like the most. It makes you want to hug someone! What is it? On another sheet of paper, draw or write a list of all the people you feel this way about.

Mike the Mailman

 M _makes the sound you hear at the beginning of the words_ **Mike** _and_ **mailman**.

Help Mike the mailman sort the mail. Find the pieces of mail that have a picture that begins with **m**. Draw a line from the picture to the bag marked with an **m**.

Nancy the Nurse

 N *makes the sound you hear at the beginning of the words* **Nancy** *and* **nurse**.

After Nancy the nurse gives a shot, she also gives a lollipop to help her young patients feel better. Color the lollipops below that have pictures beginning with **n**.

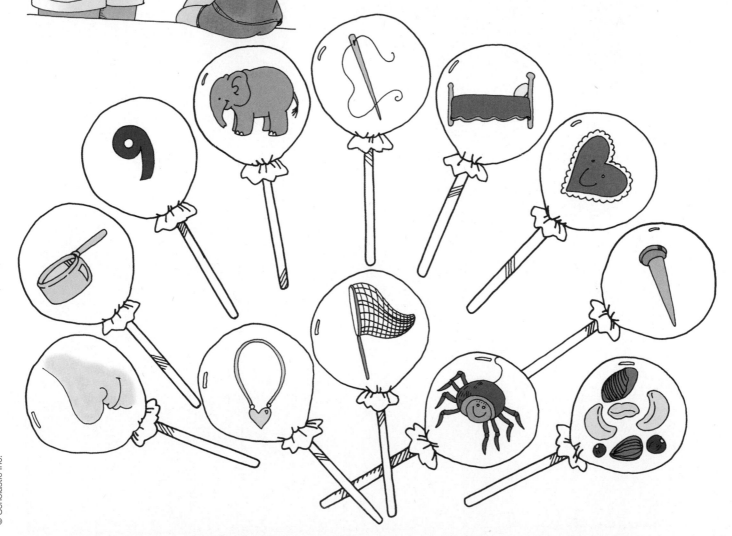

 This item begins with *n*. It is made of big sheets of paper. It has lots of pictures and words on it. It tells what is happening in the world. Grown-ups like to read it. What is it? Find one of these and look at one page of it. Find words you know. Circle them with a marker. Show a grown-up what you can read!

Patsy the Pig

 P *makes the sound you hear at the beginning of the words* **Patsy** *and* **pig**.

Help Patsy the pig find the words that begin with **p**. Use a purple crayon to write the letter **p** on top of each picture below that begins with **p**.

 This item begins with *p*. It has a head and a tail, but it is not an animal. It is a copper-colored coin. What is it? Draw it on another sheet of paper, or put one under the paper and rub over it with a crayon.

Ricky the Rabbit

R _makes the sound you hear at the beginning of the words_ **Ricky** _and_ **rabbit**.

Look at all the fun things that Ricky the rabbit can do. Circle the **r** word that tells what Ricky is doing in each picture.

rest play	swim run	ride hug
rock look	climb rake	stand roll
read sing	rope feed	rip talk
row eat	race walk	sleep rush

 This word begins with _r_. It blasts off into outer space. It orbits Earth. What is it? On another sheet of paper, draw a picture of one that has landed on the moon. Pretend you are an astronaut. Make up a story about your picture.

Silly Sally

*S makes the sound you hear at the beginning of the words **silly** and **Sally**.*

Silly Sally is looking for something that starts with **s**. You can help her find it hidden in the puzzle below. Color each space orange that has a picture in it that begins with **s**. If the picture does not begin with **s**, do not color that space.

If you take two pieces of bread and put peanut butter on one and jelly on the other, then stick them together, what have you made? It begins with *s*. Pretend you are making one by acting it out.

Tammy the Teacher

 T *makes the sound you hear at the beginning of the words* **Tammy** *and* **teacher**.

1. Trace over the letter in each row.
2. Color the pictures in each row that begin with *t*.

 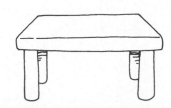  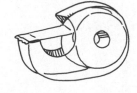

 This item begins with *t*. Campers sleep in it. What is it?

Vicki's Vacation

 V *makes the sound you hear at the beginning of the words* **Vicki** *and* **vacation**.

Vicki is going on a vacation. Help Vicki load her van with things that start with **v**. Draw a line from the **v** words to the van.

 This kind of mountain has lava inside. Sometimes the lava comes out of the top and runs down the sides. What do you call this kind of mountain? Hint: It begins with the letter *v*. On another sheet of paper, draw one and color it.

Willy the Worm

 W *makes the sound you hear at the beginning of the words* **Willy** *and* **worm**.

In the story below, there are 11 words that begin with **w**. Draw a wiggly line under each one.

> Willy the worm felt hungry. He wanted something to eat. He saw a watermelon in the window. He climbed up on the wagon. He wiggled up the wall. Then he took a bite. Wow! It was wonderful!

Now, circle each word that you underlined in the puzzle. The words go across and down.

x	w	i	g	g	l	e	d	v	t
w	a	t	e	r	m	e	l	o	n
o	g	e	k	p	r	s	b	y	w
w	o	r	m	h	f	l	x	z	i
k	n	c	w	i	n	d	o	w	l
g	v	w	a	n	t	e	d	a	l
u	w	h	s	r	z	q	g	l	y
w	o	n	d	e	r	f	u	l	a

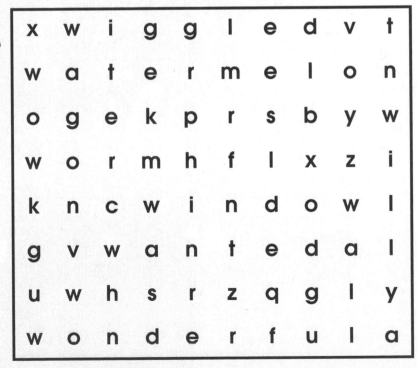

 This begins with *w*. You cannot see it, but you can feel it. Sometimes you can hear it blowing. It makes the trees sway. What is it? Now, roll up a very small piece of paper and put it on your desk. Blow on it. What happens? Why?

Yolanda's Yearbook

 Y *makes the sound you hear at the beginning of the words* **Yolanda** *and* **yearbook**.

Yolanda got a yearbook at school today. It has funny pictures in it. Which pictures go together? Draw lines to match the pictures in Yolanda's yearbook. The words in each picture begin with **y**. Can you say them?

 This word begins with y. It is one way to answer a question. When you say it, you nod your head up and down. What word is it? Now play this game. Take turns acting out these words without saying anything: *No. I don't know. Who, me? Stop! Come here. Be quiet. Too loud!*

Zachary the Zebra

 Z *makes the sound you hear at the beginning of the words* **Zachary** *and* **zebra.**

Zachary the zebra is lost! Help him find his way back to the zoo. Circle only the things that begin with **z.** Connect them to the **z**'s you find along the way.

 What word begins with z and sounds like a car speeding by very fast? (Hint: It rhymes with *broom*.) On another sheet of paper, draw a race car. Think of a story to tell with your picture.

Hidden Picture

Say the pictures in the puzzle.

Color words that begin with *t*  red

Color words that begin with *b* yellow

Color words that begin with *s* blue

Color words that begin with *d* black

 This vessel begins with *s*. It floats on the water. The wind blows it along. It is in the puzzle above. What is it? On another sheet of paper, draw a beautiful island where this could take you.

What Is a Vowel?

a b c d e f g h i j k l m n o p q r s t u v w x y z

➤ *There are 26 letters in the alphabet. Five of the letters are* **vowels**. *They are* a, e, i, o, *and* u.

Look at the alphabet train.

Color the *a* car red.
Color the *e* car blue.
Color the *i* car orange.
Color the *o* car purple.
Color the *u* car green.

➤ *Sometimes the letter* y *can be a vowel.*

Color the *y* car yellow.

Look at each store sign. Circle each vowel you can find. There are 13 of them.

Dentist

Candy Store

Bob's Burgers

Flower Shop

Bank

Abby's Apples

Vowels can make more than one sound. Each vowel has a short sound and a long sound. **Short a** *makes the sound you hear at the beginning of* **Abby** *and* **apple**. *To help you remember the short-*a *sound, stretch out the beginning of the word like this:* a-a-a-a-apple.

Abby loves to eat red apples. Help Abby find the apples that have pictures with the short-*a* sound. Color these apples red. If the picture does not have a short-*a* sound, color the apple green.

 This reptile looks like a crocodile, only smaller. It swims in the water. It begins with the short-*a* sound. What is it? On another sheet of paper, draw one in a zoo.

Find the Rhyme

Color the things in the picture that rhyme with **rat**  .

hat

shirt

pants

bat

trees

cat

mat

Think of two words that rhyme with *rat* that are not in the picture.

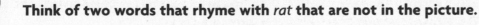

Hop Along

Help Tad Frog find his way across the pond. Color the pictures green that rhyme with **pad** .

Color the other pictures red.

Special Delivery

Help make the delivery. Follow the pictures that rhyme with **van** 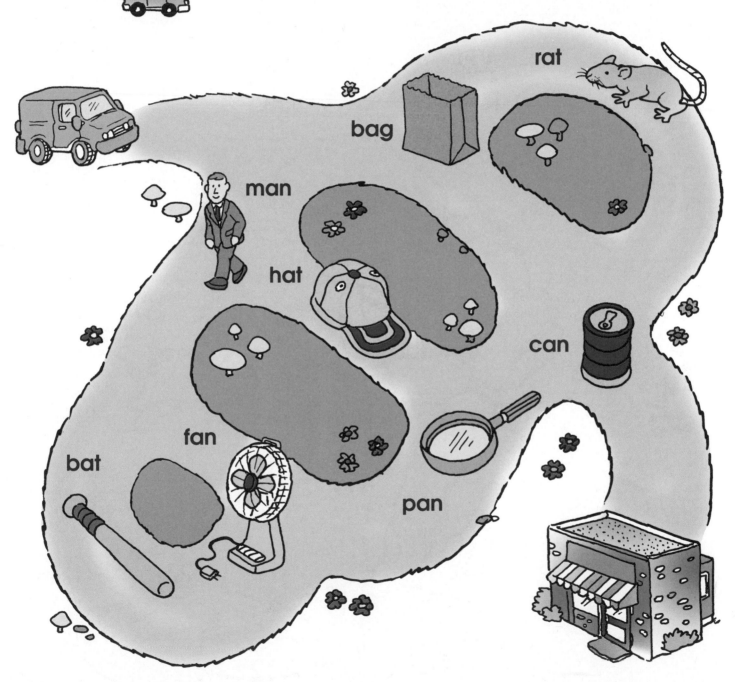.

 Count how many cans of soup you have at home.

Don't Step on the Tack!

Find and color the pictures that rhyme with **back** .

sack   **tack**   **backpack**   **crack**

 Think of two more words that rhyme with *back*. **On another sheet of paper, draw a picture of one of them.**

Picture This!

Color the picture in each row that rhymes with the first picture.

fan	hat	pan	glad
bat	man	sad	cat
sad	mad	rat	fan
sack	can	van	backpack

Rhyming Tic-Tac-Toe

Say each picture name. Find and color three pictures in a row that rhyme.

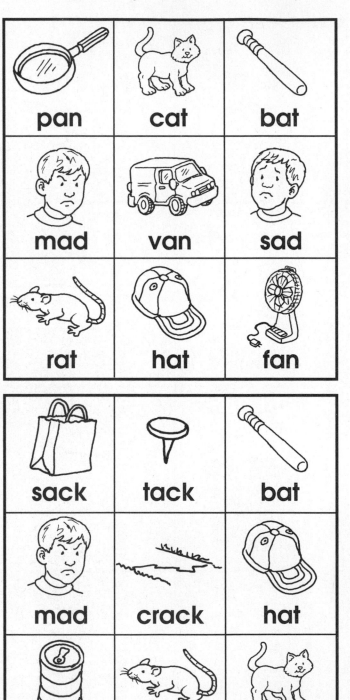

pan	cat	bat
mad	van	sad
rat	hat	fan

pad	pan	dad
sad	mad	glad
man	can	sack

sack	tack	bat
mad	crack	hat
can	rat	cat

glad	sack	crack
fan	tack	van
dad	back	hat

Ed's Eggs

 Short e *makes the sound you hear at the beginning of* **Ed** *and* **egg**. *To help you remember the short-*e *sound, stretch out the beginning of the word like this:* e-e-e-egg.

It is time for Ed to gather the eggs. Help Ed find the eggs that have pictures with the short-*e* sound. Color these eggs brown. If the picture does not have the short-*e* sound, leave the egg white.

When you say this word you nod your head up and down. It means the opposite of *no*. It has the short-*e* sound. What word is it? Think of three questions that you would answer with this word.

Farmer Ben

Color things in the picture that rhyme with **den**

hat

cat

ten

pail

dog

men

hen

pen

 Find two other things that rhyme in the picture.

Watch Out!

Help Ted find his way down the hill without hitting the shed. Follow the pictures that rhyme with **shed**.

red

bed

hen

bell

nest

pen

sled

shell

well

Finish

Taking the Pet to the Vet

Say the names of the pictures. Color the pictures that rhyme with **met** .

jet	pet	hen
sled	net	wet
bed	pen	vet

Show and Tell

 Read the story with a grown-up. Find and color the picture words in the story that rhyme with **tell**.

bell   **shell**   **yell**   **well**

It was time for Show and Tell. Bobby was so excited, he began to . Maria told about her  . Leigh had brought her favorite . Ted showed a picture of a wishing .

Flower Power

Color the pictures **red** that rhyme with **sled** .

Color the pictures **yellow** that rhyme with **ten** .

Color the pictures **blue** that rhyme with **yell** .

Color the pictures **orange** that rhyme with **net** .

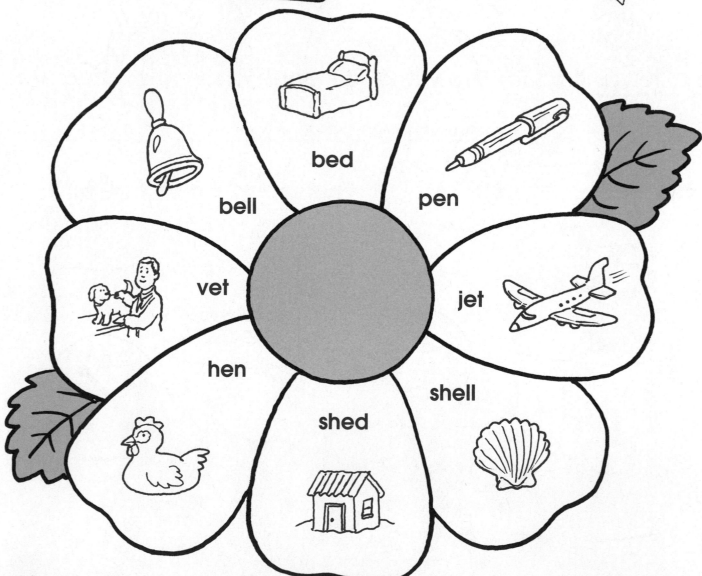

bed

pen

bell

vet

jet

hen

shed

shell

 On another sheet of paper, draw a flower with four petals. On each petal, draw something with a short-*e* sound.

Igloo Inn

Short **i** *makes the sound you hear at the beginning of* **igloo** *and* **inn**. *To help you remember the short-*i *sound, stretch out the beginning of the word like this:* i-i-i-igloo.

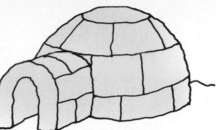

Welcome to the Igloo Inn. Color the space around the pictures with the short-*i* sound blue. If the picture does not have a short-*i* sound, draw an **X** on it.

 This is part of a baseball game. There are nine of them. The word has two short-*i* sounds. When you play baseball, someone throws a ball to a batter. This word also has a short-*i* sound. What are the two words?

Strike!

See how many bowling pins you can knock down.
Mark an **X** on the ones that rhyme with **pin**.

kick

chin

wing

grin

lick

fin

twig

Name two more words that rhyme with *pin*.

Going to the Pig Shindig

 *Read the story with a grown-up. Find and color the picture words in the story that rhyme with **big**.*

 pig    wig    twig    big

Once there was a who wanted to go to the

 shindig. She put on her pretty pink . The

 was way too . On the way to the shindig,

the got stuck on a . The  lost

her .

Fit for a King

Color the pictures that rhyme with **king** on the crown.

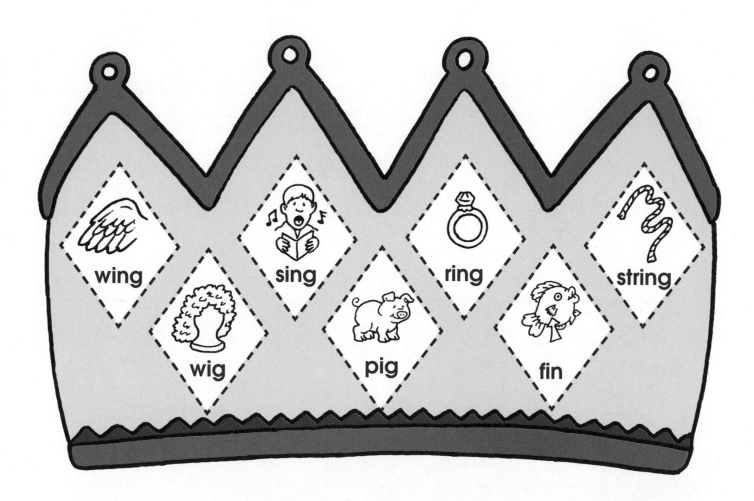

 Tell a story about a king and other things that have the *-ing* sound.

Where's the Rhyme?

Say the name of the pictures.
Color the pictures that rhyme with **lick** .

pig	king	kick
ring	sick	wig
grin	sing	brick
chick	chin	twig

Oliver's Olives

Short o *makes the sound you hear at the beginning of* **Oliver** *and* **olive***. To help you remember the short-o sound, stretch out the beginning of the word like this:* o-o-o-olive.

Oliver likes to put green olives in his salad. Help Oliver find the olives that have pictures with the short-o sound. Color these olives green. If the picture does not have the short-o sound, color the olive black.

 This creature lives in the sea. It has eight arms. Its head looks like a balloon. It begins with the short-o sound. What is it? Tell what you could do if you had eight arms!

Freddy the Frog

 *Read the story with a grown-up. Find and color the picture words in the story that rhyme with **jog**.*

frog

log

dog

hog

Freddy is a very large bull . He is as big as

a . His best friends are a bull  and a

. Together they play leap . See them

jump over the .

Under the Big Top

Say the names of the pictures in the balls.
Color the pictures that rhyme with **pop**

 On another sheet of paper, draw a picture about this sentence: Mop up the soda pop.

Dot the Robot

Circle the things in the picture that rhyme with **knot** .

pot   spot   hot   dot

 Think of one more word that rhymes with *knot*.

Sherlock's Clues

Help Sherlock find the way to the missing lock. Color the pictures that rhyme with **clock**.

clock	sock	log	dog
mop	rock	knock	hog
pot	spot	block	lock

© Scholastic Inc.

My Uncle's Umbrella

 Short u *makes the sound you hear at the beginning of* **uncle** *and* **umbrella**. *To help you remember the short-*u *sound, stretch out the beginning of the word like this:* u-u-u-umbrella.

My uncle needs to buy a new umbrella! Help him find the umbrellas that have pictures with the short-*u* sound. Color these umbrellas with red and blue stripes. If the picture does not have the short-*u* sound, write *NO* on the umbrella.

Let's Dance!

 *Read the story with a grown-up. Find and color the picture words in the story that rhyme with **dug**.*

rug   bug   mug   hug

Once there was was a lady . She liked to dance on

a 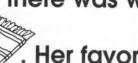. Her favorite dance was the jitter . She won a

first-place . Everyone gave her a  for being the

best dancing lady .

© Scholastic Inc.

Hit a Home Run!

Randy hit a home run. Start at home plate and color the bases that rhyme with **fun**.

The Stuck Duck

Help the duck across the pond. Color the pictures that rhyme with **duck**.

sun

truck

bun

hug

puck

rug

duck

bug

mug

yuck

run

Rhyme and Color

Color the pictures yellow that rhyme with **luck**.
Color the pictures blue that rhyme with **rug**.
Color the pictures orange that rhyme with **run**.

bird

sun

hug

boy

shell

ball

duck

truck

shoes

bun

mug

bug

Short Vowel Crosswords

Use the picture clues to add a short vowel to each puzzle.

1.

```
W
P N
  G
```

2.

```
  T
C   P
  B
```

3.

```
H
B   D
  N
```

4.

```
  T
F   X
  P
```

5.

```
  F
B   T
  N
```

Short Vowel Tic-Tac-Toe

Say the picture names.
Find and color 3 pictures in a row with the same short vowel sound.

1. Short-*a* Sound as in

2. Short-*i* Sound as in

3. Short-*e* Sound as in

City C and Country C

 C *can make two sounds. If the vowels* **e** *or* **i** *come after the* **c**, *then* **c** *will have the* **s** *sound. If one of the other vowels (***a, o, u***) comes after the* **c**, *then* **c** *will have the* **k** *sound.*

Look at the pictures and words on this page. If it begins with an **s** sound, as in *city*, circle **s**. If it begins with a **k** sound, as in *country*, circle **k**.

couch	centipede	cow	cinnamon roll
k s	k s	k s	k s
corn	**cent**	**cereal**	**coat**
k s	k s	k s	k s
cake	**ceiling**	**cobra**	**cat**
k s	k s	k s	k s
celery	**coconut**	**circles**	**comb**
k s	k s	k s	k s

Use the words from the previous page.
Write each word that begins with the same sound as *city*.

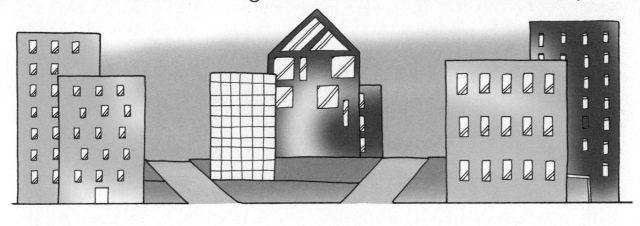

_____   _____   _____

_____   _____   _____

_____

Write each word that begins with the same sound as *country*.

_____   _____   _____

_____   _____   _____

This word has two *c*'s in it. The first *c* sounds like an *s*. The other one sounds like a *k*. It is a fun place to see a show. There are clowns and elephants in a big tent. People do amazing tricks. What is it? On another sheet of paper, draw a picture of yourself doing a trick there.

Gary the Goat and George the Giraffe

G can make two sounds. Usually, words that begin with g *make the same sound that you hear in* **Gary** *and* **goat**. *But sometimes a* g *can sound like a* j, *as in* **George** *and* **giraffe**. *This usually happens when the vowels* e *or* i *come after the* g, *but not always. The best way to figure out which* g *sound to use is to try both sounds and see which one makes sense. For example, try saying* goat *with both* g *sounds. See? One of them does not make sense!*

Look at each picture below. If the picture begins like *goat*, circle **g**. If the picture begins like *giraffe*, circle **j**.

gate	girl	gingerbread man	gift
g j	g j	g j	g j
giant	**guitar**	**gum**	**gerbil**
g j	g j	g j	g j
goose	**gorilla**	**general**	**gymnast**
g j	g j	g j	g j

Use the words from the previous page. On the goat, write each word that begins with the same sound as *Gary*.

On the giraffe, write each word that begins with the same sound as *George*.

This word begins with a *g* that sounds like a *j*. It is a huge room. You can sit in the bleachers and watch a basketball game there. Most high schools have one. What is it? Think of another game that can be played there. On another sheet of paper, draw a picture of it.

Queen Q and Her Maidservant U

 Q *makes the sound you hear at the beginning of the word* **queen***.*

Queen **Q** is very special. She has a maidservant named **U**. When Queen **Q** and Maidservant **U** work together, they make a sound that sounds like *kw*.

In each crown, write the word from the Word Box that matches the picture. (Hint: Do the easy ones first!)

Word Box

question   quiet   quarrel

quarter   quack   quail   quilt

 This word begins with *q*. **Sometimes a teacher gives one to see if the students know their spelling words. It is another word for** *test*. **It rhymes with** *Liz*. **What is it? At playtime, pretend to be a teacher. Ask someone to be your student. Ask them questions. Then change places.**

© Scholastic Inc.

Superhero X to the Rescue

 X makes the sound of ks. *(Hint: Say the word* kiss *very fast!) Most of the time, an* x *is in the middle or at the end of a word.*

Help Superhero X put the missing **x** in each word. Then draw a line to the matching picture.

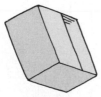

fo___

mi___er

ta___i

e___it

a___

si___

o___

bo___

e___ercise

tu___edo

 It begins with *x*. It is a special kind of picture that a doctor takes so that she can see your bones. What is it? See if you can feel the bones in your fingers and hands. Make them wiggle!

Animal Tails

Consonants can come at the beginning, middle, or end of a word. To help you hear the ending sound, say the word and stretch out the last sound. For example, when you see the picture of the bear, say "bear-r-r-r-r."

Say the name of each animal. Write the ending sound in the box by its tail.

 This creature lives in the sea. It does not have a tail. It has eight arms. Its head looks like a balloon. It ends with s. What is it? On another sheet of paper, draw one eating eight candy canes.

Larry Last

Help Larry Last find the last sound that each word makes. Circle the correct letter under each lunchbox.

k   n   s

r   g   l

s   f   r

n   d   z

b   m   n

t   k   p

k   f   d

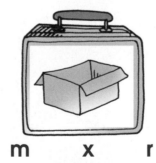

m   x   r

g   z   l

d   v   r

l   k   d

g   t   f

You do this while you are asleep. It is like watching a movie in your head. It ends with *m*. What is it? On another sheet of paper, draw a picture about one that you have had. Tell about it.

© Scholastic Inc.

Consonant Caboose

Find two words on each train that end with the same sound. Color them. Then write the letter of the ending sound in the caboose.

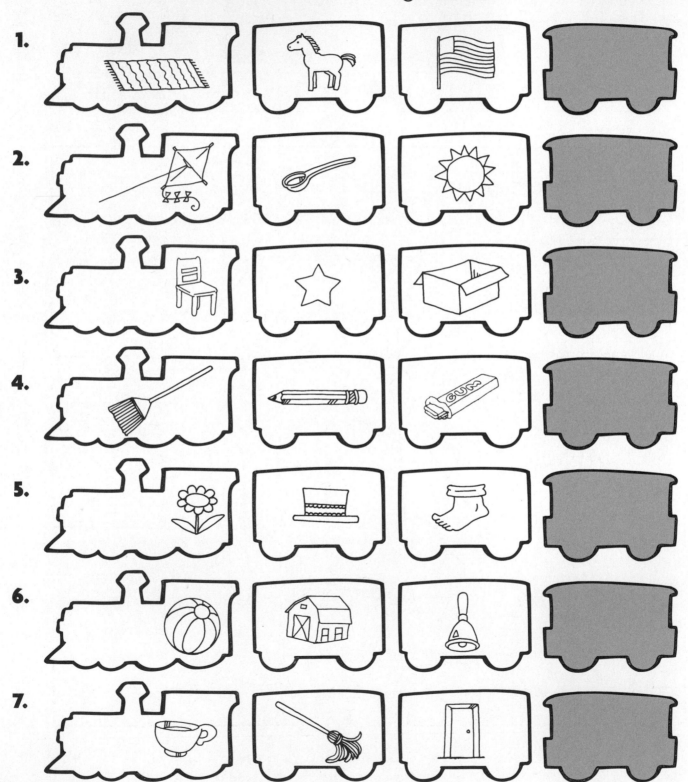

What Do You See?

Say the words.
Listen for the ending sounds.
Use the Ending Sounds Color Code to make a picture.

Ending Sounds Color Code

| **blue = s** | **green = t** | **black = d** | **red = l** | **white = m** |

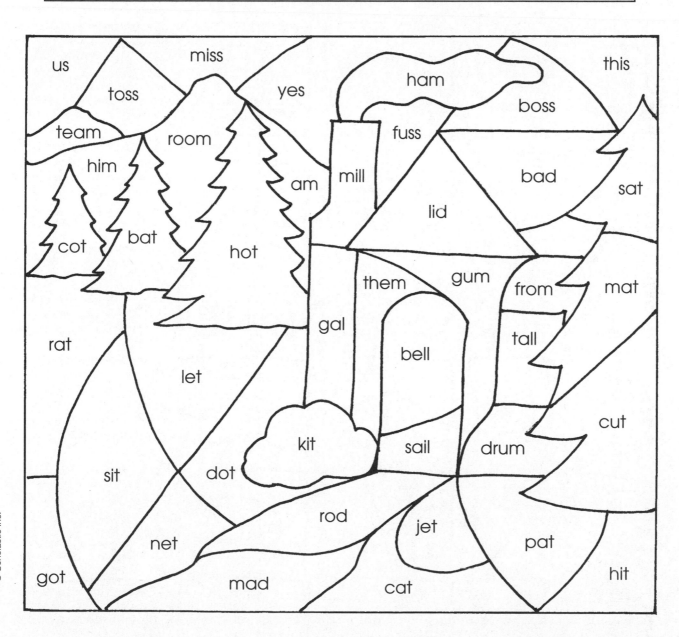

Amy's Aprons

Every vowel has a long sound and a short sound. **Long a** makes the sound you hear at the beginning of **Amy** and **apron**. To help remember the long-a sound, stretch out the beginning of the word like this: a-a-a-a-apron.

Amy needs a new apron. Help Amy find the aprons that have pictures with the long-*a* sound. Color these aprons pink. If the picture on an apron does not have a long-*a* sound, color it purple.

There is a first one, a second one, and a third one. When you hit the baseball, you run and step on them. The word has the long-*a* sound. What is it? On another sheet of paper, draw a baseball field. Draw arrows that point to your answer.

Don't Forget Your Skates!

Find and color the things that rhyme with **ate**

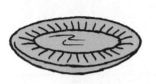
plate

skate

gate

 Say a girl's name that rhymes with *ate*.

Jake the Snake

Color the pictures below that rhyme with **snake** 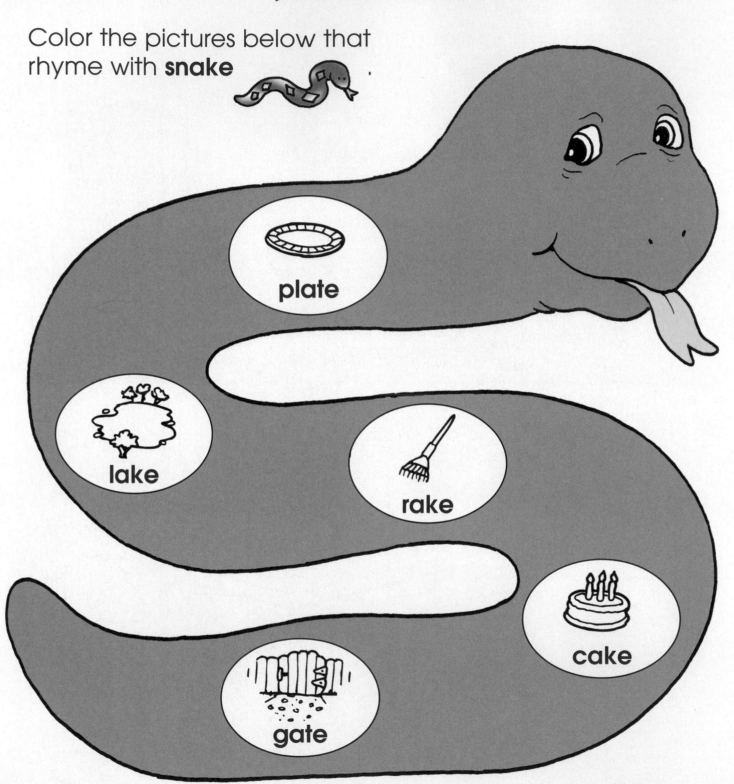.

A Day at the Beach

  *Read the story with a grown-up. Find and color the picture words in the story that rhyme with **nail**.*

pail   trail   snail   nail   sail

Sam was walking down the . He was looking for

things to put in his . The first thing Sam saw was a

. He picked up the and put it in his .

Farther down the  Sam saw a . He put the

 in the . Sam had room for one more thing in

his 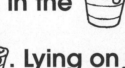. Lying on the  was a boat

with a broken 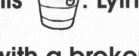.

Color the Rhyme

Color the pictures **red** that rhyme with **lake** .

Color the pictures **yellow** that rhyme with **ate** .

Color the pictures **blue** that rhyme with **sail** .

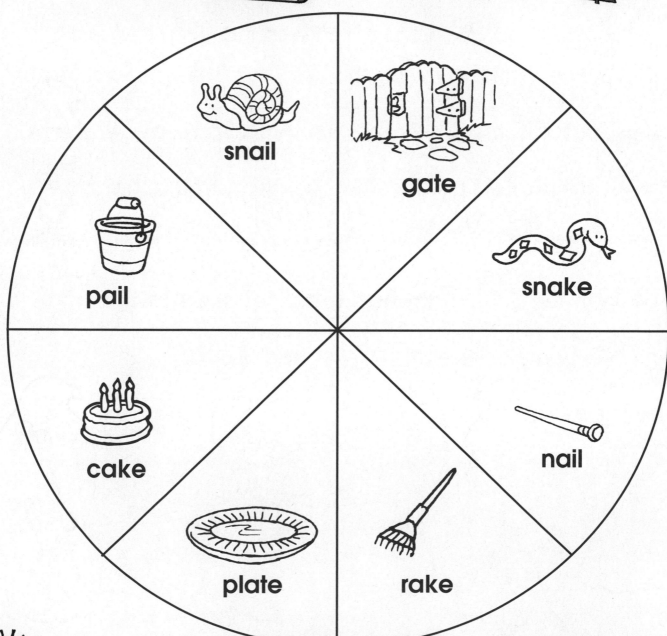

 On another sheet of paper, draw a picture of something else that rhymes with *snail*.

Ethan's Eagle

Long e *makes the sound you hear at the beginning of* **Ethan** *and* **eagle***. To help you remember the long-*e* sound, stretch out the beginning of the word like this:* e-e-e-eagle.

Ethan's eagle is lonely. He needs a friend. Help Ethan find the eagles that have pictures with the long-*e* sound. Color these eagles brown. If the picture on an eagle does not have a long-*e* sound, write *NO* on it.

 You have one of these on the end of your pencil. It is made of rubber. You need it when you make a mistake! It begins with the long-*e* sound. What is it? Write your name with a pencil. Now rub it off with the answer to the riddle.

What Do You See at the Park?

Color the things in the picture that rhyme with **see**.

bee   **knee**   **three**   **tree**

On another sheet of paper, draw a picture of something that makes you shout with glee.

Beep, Beep

In each row, cross out the pictures that do not rhyme with **beep** .

bell	**jeep**	**knee**
sheep	**shell**	**tree**
three	**jet**	**sleep**
hen	**shed**	**sweep**

 Name the nursery rhyme that tells about a girl who lost her sheep.

Ivan's Ice

 Long i *makes the sound you hear at the beginning of* **ice**. *To help you remember the long-*i *sound, stretch out the beginning of the word like this:* i-i-i-ice.

It is so hot today! Ivan needs some ice in his drink. Help Ivan find the ice cubes that have pictures with the long-*i* sound. Outline these ice cubes in blue. If the picture on an ice cube does not have a long-*i* sound, draw a puddle of water around it to make it look like it is melting.

 This is something your lips do when you are happy. It is another word for *grin*. **It has the long-***i* **sound. What is it? On another sheet of paper, draw a picture of your face with one of these on it.**

Be Mine!

Color the hearts with pictures that rhyme with **valentine** .

vine

hive

nine
9

Be
Mine

line

ice

pine

 Make a valentine that says *Be mine,* **and give it to somebody special .**

For the Right Price

Find and color the things that rhyme with **price**  .

mice

string

ice

rice

button

vine

dice

cheese

Buzzy Bees

Help the bees find the way back home. Follow the pictures that rhyme with **hive** 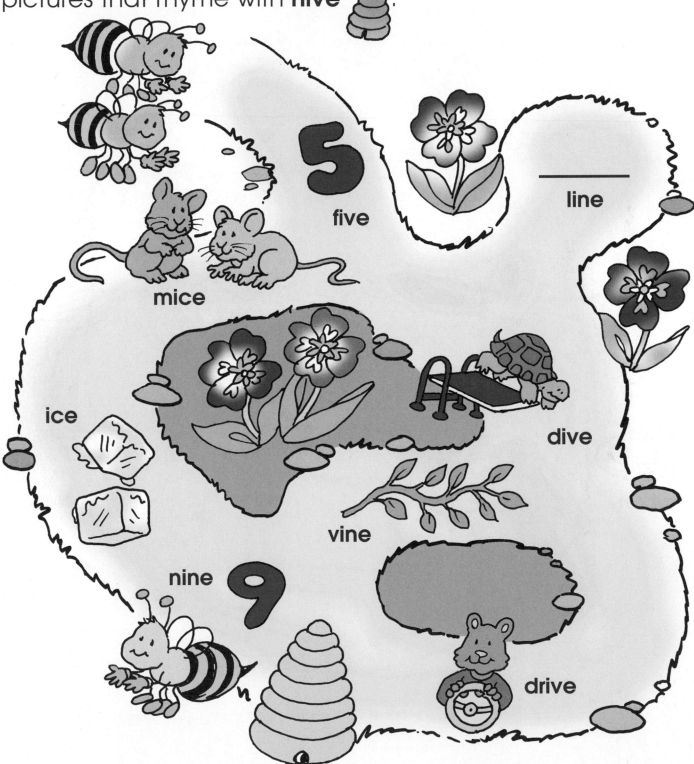.

Rhyme Time

Draw lines to connect the pictures that rhyme.

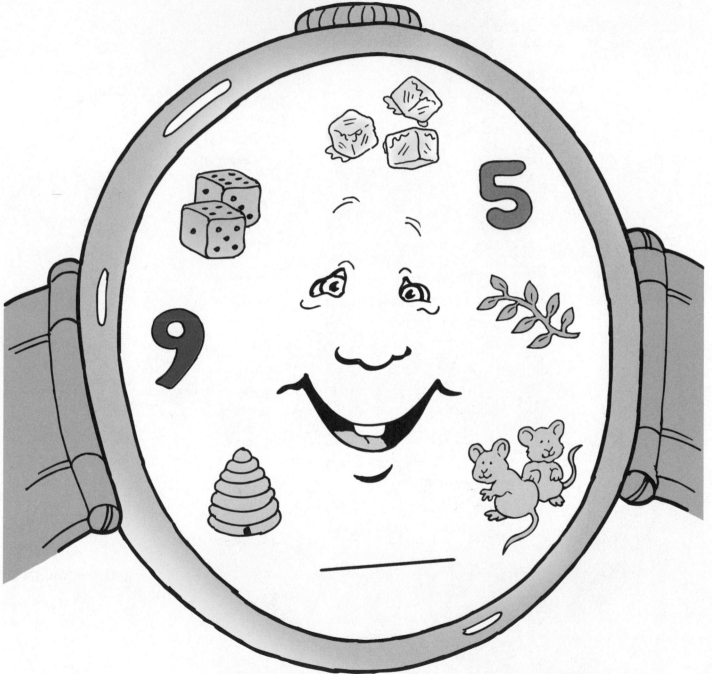

 Make your own rhyming clock. Think of three new sets of rhyming pictures. On another sheet of paper, draw them in a clock.

Miss Ova's Ovals

 Long o *makes the sound you hear at the beginning of* **Ova** *and* **oval**. *To help you remember the long-o sound, stretch out the beginning of the word like this:* o-o-o-oval.

Miss Ova is teaching her class about shapes. Today they learned about ovals. Draw an oval around the pictures that have the long-*o* sound. If the picture does not have a long-*o* sound, draw a square around it.

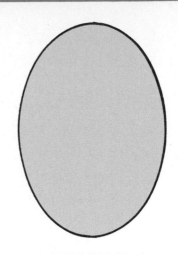

 You might see this word on a sign in the window of a store. It lets you know you can go inside. It is the opposite of *closed*. **It begins with a long-o sound. What is the word? On another sheet of paper, make one of these signs and decorate it.**

Construction Zone

Help the digger fill the right dump trucks. Color the trucks that have pictures that rhyme with **stone**

cone

phone

nose

coat

bone

Row, Row, Row Your Boat

Help the rowboat find the shore. Color the pictures that rhyme with **float** 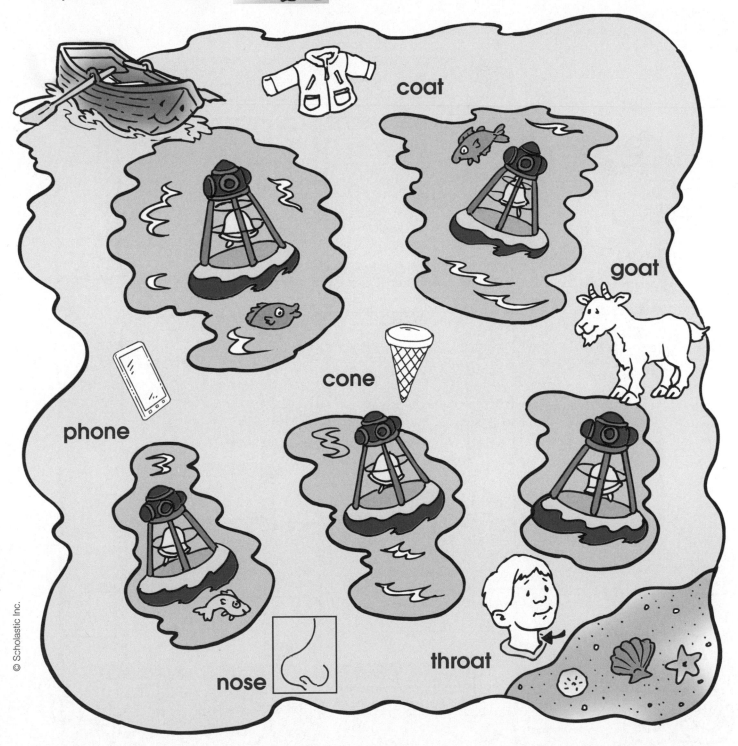 .

coat

goat

cone

phone

nose

throat

Mighty Firefighter

Help the firefighter put out the fire. Color the pictures in the windows that rhyme with **hose** blue. Color the other windows red.

rose

coat

cone

nose

close

goat

Unicorn University

➤ **Long u** *makes the sound you hear at the beginning of* **unicorn**. *To help you remember the long-*u* sound, stretch out the beginning of the word like this:* u-u-u-unicorn.

This unicorn is smart! He goes to Unicorn University. Find every book that has a picture with the long-*u* sound. Color these books blue. If the picture does not have a long-*u* sound, draw an **X** on it.

1. Turn in your work.
2. No talking in class.
3. Raise your hand.
4. Keep your desk clean.

💡 **This is the name of a country. It is made up of 50 states. Its president lives in Washington, D.C. The first word begins with a long-*u* sound. What country is it? On another sheet of paper, draw the flag of this country.**

Long-u Word Fruit

Look at the word on each piece of fruit. Fill in the blank to make a rhyming word. Read your words to a friend.

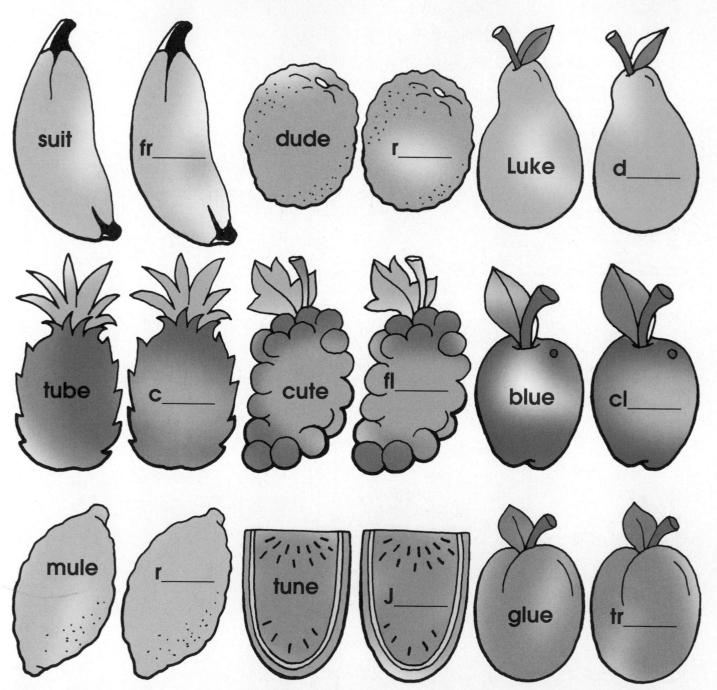

suit

fr_____

dude

r_____

Luke

d_____

tube

c_____

cute

fl_____

blue

cl_____

mule

r_____

tune

J_____

glue

tr_____

 This is the color of the sky and the sea. It has a long-*u* sound. What is it? Think of something else that is this color. On another sheet of paper, draw and color it.

Long Vowel Tic-Tac-Toe

Say the picture names.
Find and color 3 pictures in a row with the same long vowel sound.

1. Long-*e* sound

2. Long-*i* sound

3. Long-*o* sound

Time for Rhymes

Say the name of each picture. Circle the two pictures that rhyme in each group.

© Scholastic Inc.

Check the Signs

Say the name of each picture. Circle the animal with the picture that rhymes with the first picture in each row.

Be a Word Builder!

Make your own rhyming words. Look at the picture and say the word. Copy the word. Then change the first letter using each of the letters on the hammer to make new words.

p s r m f h b

h c m t w f

f j l h

s l b

ball

cat

dog

hand

💡 **This word rhymes with *fish*. It rhymes with *dish*. It is what you make when you blow out the candles on your birthday cake! What is it? Draw yours on another sheet of paper.**

Scholastic Success With

SCIENCE

Healthy Treats to Eat

Fruits and **vegetables** help our bodies grow big and strong. Say the name of each picture. Then follow the fruits and vegetables to move through the maze.

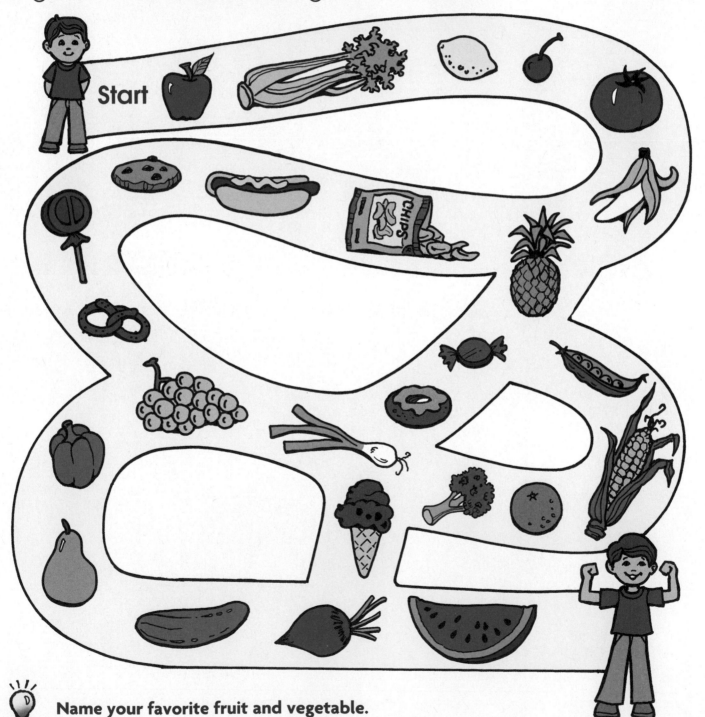

Start

Name your favorite fruit and vegetable.

What Do Bears Eat?

Look at the pictures. Circle the things that bears eat.

Winter Sleepers

Who hibernates? Name the sleeping animals below.
Then find them in the big picture.

turtle   **chipmunk**   **bear**   **frog**   **bat**   **snake**

Nocturnal Animals

Nocturnal animals stay awake at night. Can you find 5 nocturnal animals. Circle them. Then color the picture.

Inside a Chipmunk's Burrow

Look at the diagram. Then follow the directions.

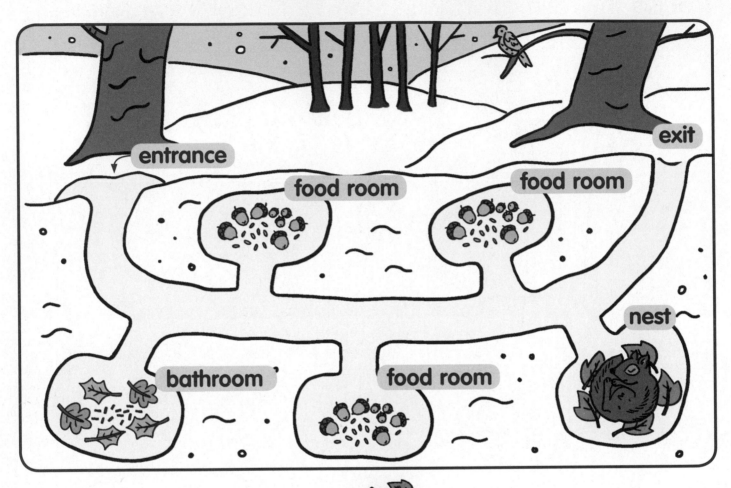

1. (Circle) the .

   chipmunk

2. Put ✔s on the 🥜🥜.

   food rooms

3. Put an ✗ on the 🍂.

   bathroom

4. Put a ☺ on the entrance.

Armored (With Shell) or Not!

Animals with shells are called **crustaceans**. Draw a circle around the animals that have shells. Color the pictures.

Rough Reptiles

Animals covered with rough, dry skin belong to the **reptile** family. Trace to make reptiles. Color.

 Name each reptile.

© Scholastic Inc.

Mammal Mix-Up

Animals with hair belong to the **mammal** family.
Mark an X on the animal in each row that does not
belong to the mammal family.

💡 **Did you know you are a mammal? On another sheet of paper,
draw a picture of you and your favorite mammal.**

Tracks in the Snow

This chart shows what some animal tracks look like.
(Circle) the answer to each question.

animal	**deer** 	**dog**	**rabbit**
track			

1. Whose tracks are these?

2. Whose tracks are these?

3. Whose tracks are these?

Shark Diagram

A **diagram** shows the parts of
something. The labels name the parts.
Draw the missing parts on the shark.
Then trace the words to make labels.

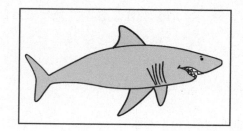

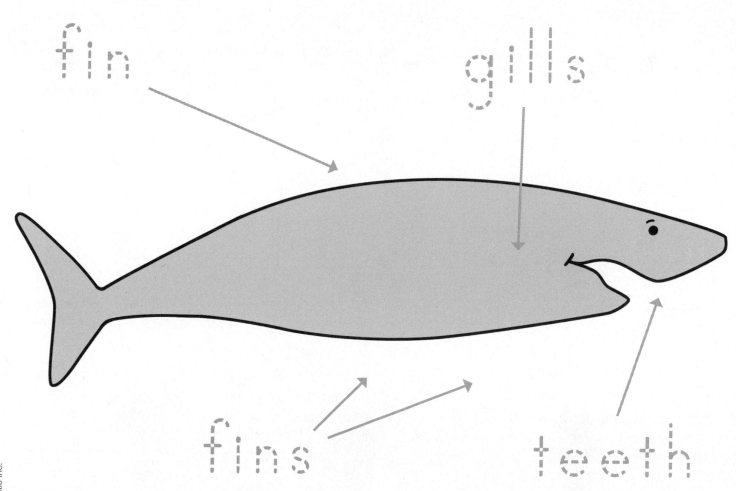

fin

gills

fins

teeth

Insects Have Six Legs

An ant is an insect. Count its legs.

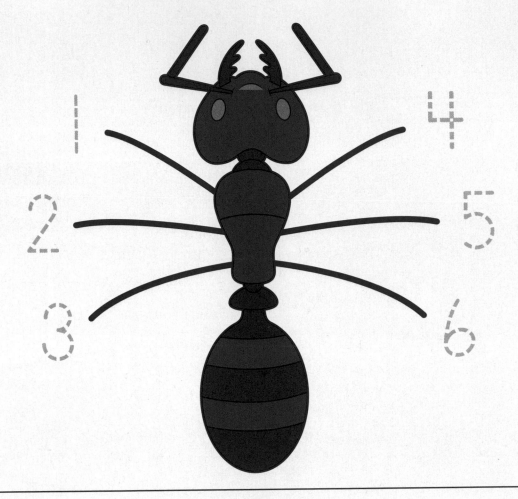

Draw six legs on each of these ants.

Bird Body Diagram

Label each part of the bird to complete
the diagram. Use the words in the Word Bank.

Word Bank
beak
eye
wing
tail
foot

Plants Grow Above and Below

Read the sentences and finish the pictures.

Stems and leaves
grow up.
Draw the **leaves**.

Tree trunks
grow up.
Draw the **trunk**.

Carrot leaves
grow up.
Draw the **leaves**.

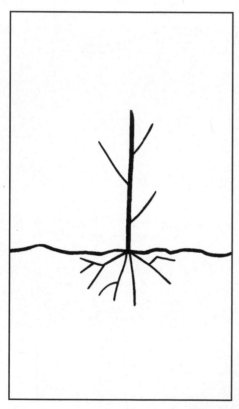

Roots
grow down.
Draw more **roots**.

Tree roots
grow down.
Draw more **roots**.

Carrots
grow down.
Draw the **carrot**.

© Scholastic Inc.

A Carrot Grows

How does a carrot grow?
Number the pictures to show the order.

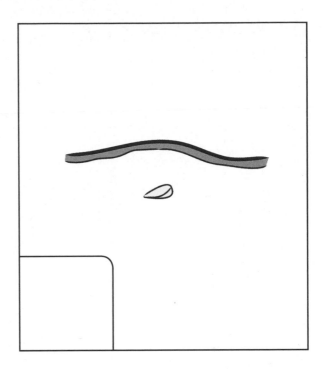

What Do Plants Need?

Draw lines from the plant to the pictures of things that it needs to live.

water

air

hat

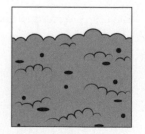

cookies

sun

soil

© Scholastic Inc.

Signs of Spring

Circle the things you see in the spring.

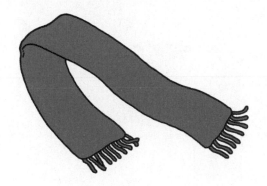

Signs of Fall

Circle the things you see in the fall.

Weather Outside My Window

Read each weather word. Draw what you would see out your window in that kind of weather.

sunny

cloudy

rainy

windy

Can Wind Move It?

Make wind by blowing through a straw!
Predict which objects your wind will move. Then find out.

	YES 👍	NO 👎
cotton ball		
crayon		
block		
leaf		
rock		
tissue box		
Draw your own item.		
Draw your own item.		

ITTY-BITTY
WORD BOOKS

How to Assemble the Word Books

1. Tear out each page along the perforation.

2. Cut along the dashed lines; fold along the solid lines.

3. Place the pages in order and staple along the spine.

I live in

_____

16

My Little

Neighborhood Book

1

traffic
light

14

house

3

post office

12

firehouse

5

car

10

police
officer

7

school

2

school bus

15

store

4

stop sign

13

police
station

6

mail
carrier

11

firefighter

8

flag

9

scarecrow

16

My Little Book of

Farm Words

1

goat

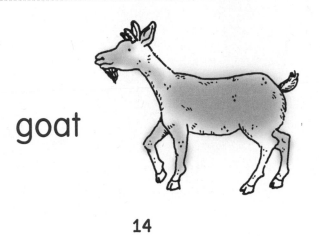

14

cow

3

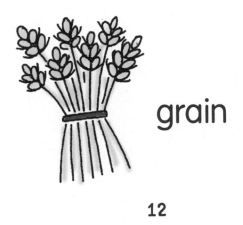

grain

12

sheep

5

tractor

10

horse

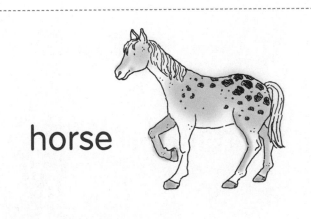

7

© Scholastic Inc.

barn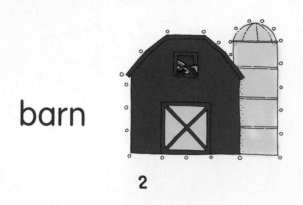

2

farmer

rooster

4

 chicken

13

milk

6

egg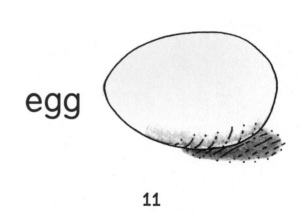

11

duck

8

pig

9

I made this mini-book
in the month of

_____

16

Month-by-Month
Mini-Book

1

New Year

14

February

3

November

12

April

5

September

10

June

7

 January

2

 seasons

15

 March

4

December

13

 May

6

 October

11

 July

8

August

9

My favorite fruit:

_____

My favorite vegetable:

_____

16

My Tiny Book of

Fruits & Vegetables

1

corn

14

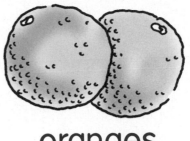

oranges

3

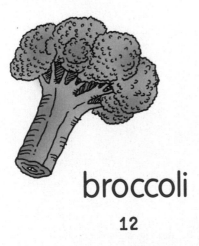

broccoli

12

banana

5

pears

10

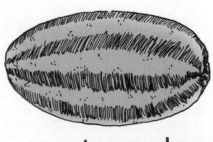

watermelon

7

apples

2

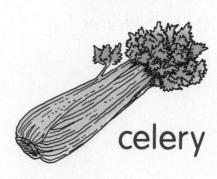

celery

15

lemons

4

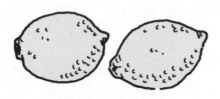

peas

13

strawberries

6

carrot

11

pineapple

8

grapes

9

© Scholastic Inc.

My favorite way to
travel is by

_____

16

Transportation Words

1

wagon

14

bus

3

truck

12

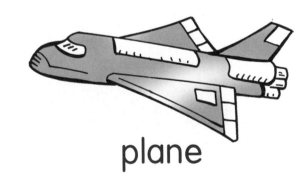

plane

5

running

10

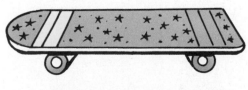

skateboard

7

car

2

rocket

15

train

4

van

13

bike

6

scooter

11

ship

8

walking

9

My favorite big animal is:

_____

16

My Little Book of
Big Animals

1

ostrich

14

polar bear

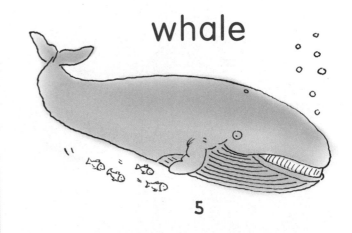

3

dinosaur

12

whale

5

tiger

10

jaguar

7

elephant
2

camel
15

rhinoceros
4

panda

horse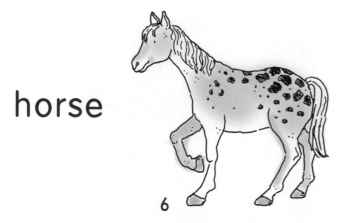
6

zebra
11

buffalo
8

moose
9

I would like a

_____

for a pet.

16

© Scholastic Inc.

iguana

14

snake

12

parakeet

10

Pets

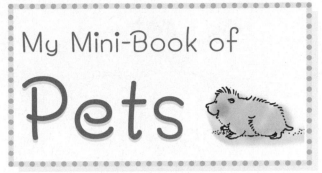

1

dog

3

gerbil

5

mouse

7

cat

2

an imaginary pet!

15

frog

4

rabbit

13

hamster

6

parrot

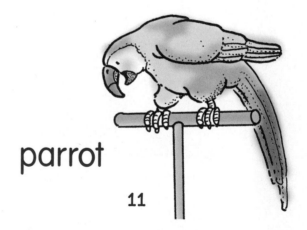

11

fish

8

turtle

9

Right now I feel

_____

16

Feelings & Faces

1

angry

14

sad

3

silly

12

mad

5

sleepy

10

worried

7

frustrated

2

 funny face!

15

happy

4

calm

13

content

6

nervous

11

surprised

8

excited

9

My favorite shape is

_____

16

box

14

square

3

ball

12

oval

5

© Scholastic Inc.

cube

10

octagon

7

circle

2

cylinder

15

rectangle

4

pentagon

13

triangle

6

hexagon

11

diamond

8

star

9

crayons

16

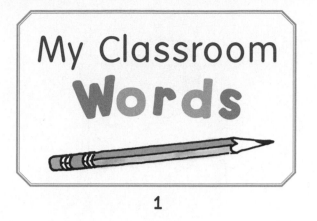

My Classroom Words

1

scissors

14

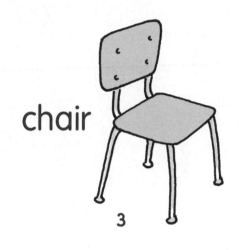

chair

3

door

12

teacher

5

clock

10

book

7

© Scholastic Inc.

 desk

2

blocks

15

easel

4

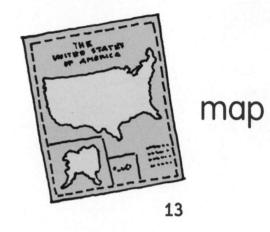 map

13

 student

6

 glue

11

notebook

8

pencil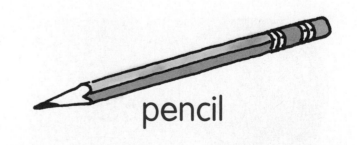

9

My favorite color is:

_____

16

Rainbow in Your Pocket!

1

markers

14

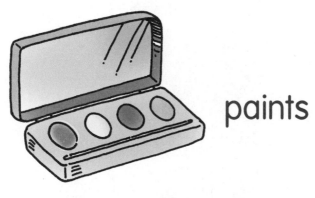

green

3

paints

12

blue

5

black

10

brown

7

red

2

pencils

15

yellow

4

crayons

CRAYONS

13

orange

6

rainbow

11

purple

8

pink

9